What's So Funny About®... OR Nursing?

A Creative Approach to
Celebrating Your Profession

By RN, Neurohumorist &
Speaker Hall of Fame inductee
Karyn Buxman

Cover design by Poole Communications
573-221-3635 | www.PooleCommunications.com

Medical studies show that people who use humor have lower levels of the stress hormones epinephrine and norepinephrine.

What's So Funny About . . .? Publishing
800-848-6679 | www.KarynBuxman.com

"Caring is the essence of nursing."

~ Jean Watson, RN

"Caring is part of the art of nursing.
Humor is part of the art of caring."

~ Karyn Buxman, RN

Disclaimer

I, Karyn Buxman, RN, MSN, CSP, CPAE, LOL, FYI, CIA, PDQ, OMG, am a neurohumorist and a nurse, but not a medical doctor—or *any* kind of doctor, for that matter. For diagnosis or treatment of any medical problem (real or imagined), consult a real doctor (*not* Doctor Seuss, Doctor Dolittle or Doctor Who). The information provided in this book is designed to provide helpful information on the subjects discussed; it is not meant to be used, nor should it be used (not even once), to diagnose or treat any medical condition. The publisher and author are not responsible for any health conditions, nor are they liable for any damages or negative consequences from any treatment or action, to any person reading or following the advice contained in this book. Readers should be aware that references are provided for informational purposes only. Readers should be aware that the medical and neurological fields evolve and change. Readers should also be aware that a spoonful of sugar makes the medicine go down.

Furthermore . . . This book is not intended to be used as a flotation device. This book is not intended for dummies. Nor for idiots. This book may be harmful if swallowed. It contains a substantial amount of non-active ingredients. Not recommended for children under 12. Batteries not included. Keep away from open flame. Colors may vary and, in time, fade. Storage temperature: -30 C (-22F) to 40C (104F). Beware of dog. Slippery when wet. You must be present to win. Use only in well-ventilated areas. Driver does not carry cash. Tag not to be removed under penalty of law. Do not read while driving or operating heavy machinery. Do not read while sleeping. Do not fold, spindle or mutilate. Do not expose to direct sunlight. Do not puncture or incinerate. Do not pass Go. Do not collect $200.

Void where prohibited by law. Or by local custom. Or by your mom. Look both ways before crossing. No smoking. No parking. No standing. No way. Practice safe sex. But remember that practice makes perfect. And remember to send your mother a card on her birthday. Please affix proper postage. Alcohol content is less than 12% by volume. Do not drink and drive. Do not drink and read. But it's okay to drink and watch TV. Content is rated PG-13 by the Academy for Butting Into Other People's Business. Do your civic duty and vote. Do not submerge in water. Kilroy was here. Follow your doctor's recommendations. Follow your heart. Follow the Yellow Brick Road. Good grief, Charlie Brown! Use your Zip Code! Stop! Look! And Listen! Don't over-use exclamation marks! Don't end sentences with prepositions. Or propositions. Don't try this at home. Seek professional advice. Where's the beef? Where's Waldo? Where oh where has my little dog gone?

Authorized personnel only. An apple a day keeps the doctor away. Do not eat of the fruit of the Tree of Knowledge of Good and Evil. Objects appear smaller than they really are. Because I said so, that's why. Fragile. This side up. Handle with care. Put your right arm in, put your right arm out, put your right arm in, and shake it all about. You do the Hokey-Pokey and you turn yourself around. (That's what it's all about.)

Watching a sitcom can increase HDL (good cholesterol) by 26%, and decrease C-reactive proteins (harmful proteins) by 66%.

Don't run with scissors. Don't feed the animals. Don't mix plaids with stripes. Don't have a cow, man. Don't call me Shirley. Do no evil. Do unto others as you would have them do unto you. Open sesame. Open wide. Open the pod bay doors please, Hal. Houston, we have a problem. E.T. phone home. There's no place like home. Home, home on the range. How to Make Friends and Influence People. How to Succeed in Business Without Really Trying. May cause dizziness. But—thank god!—will not cause constipation.

Watch for falling rocks. Watch your P's and Q's. What, me worry? Who's on first? This offer expires after 30 days. Best if used by March 31. No trespassing. Dangerous curves ahead. Deer Xing. Merry Xmas. X marks the spot. X-rated. XOXO. Riders under 54-inches must be accompanied by an adult. 25 mpg city, 43 mpg highway. 25 or 6 to 4. The answer to life, the universe, and everything: 42. Contents may settle in shipping. Results may vary. Lather. Rinse. Repeat.

This disclaimer disclaims the disclamation of its disclaimancy. And in the end . . . The love you take is equal to the love you make.

"Finally, here is a book that takes the evidence-based research of psychoneuroimmunology and makes it applicable for therapeutic benefit in patient care. As a nurse, Karyn takes the reader on a journey of the 'mind-body connection' with the use of the positive behavior—humor! And, she tells you what humor really can do for you! Karyn's approach makes the reading not only humorous but also fun and playful . . . these all translate into beneficial physiology . . . so enjoy your journey, it is different yet therapeutic because . . . 'he who laughs lasts'!"

~ LEE S. BERK, DRPH, MPH, FACSM, FAAIM, CHES, DIRECTOR, MOLECULAR RESEARCH LAB., SCHOOL OF ALLIED HEALTH; PROFESSOR, SCHOOLS OF ALLIED HEALTH, GRADUATE & MEDICINE, LOMA LINDA UNIVERSITY

"Karyn Buxman is a thought leader and master communicator in the field of applied humor. And . . . she makes me laugh!"

~ DR. HEIDI HANNA, AUTHOR OF THE SHARP SOLUTION

"*What's So Funny About* OR *Nursing is a groundbreaking book. It focuses on using healthy humor to combat stress and promote healing. Karyn Buxman is a gifted author, speaker and a nurse who shares the lighter side of the latest research in coping with illness. This is an invaluable resource for caregivers.*"

~ MARY KAY MORRISON, MSED, AUTHOR OF *USING HUMOR TO MAXIMIZE LIVING*

"Five pages into this wonderful book, my cholesterol was down, my blood pressure dropped, and I dropped 50 pounds!"

~ Elvis

"I wish Karyn Buxman was my mother."

~ Freud

"I tip my hat to 'the other humorist from Hannibal, Missouri'! Karyn Buxman has written The Great American Non-Fiction Advice Book!"

~ Twain

"Follow the Yellow Brick Road! And, follow Karyn Buxman's advice!"

~ Glinda

"To be (funny),
Or not to be (funny).
That is the question."

~ Hamlet

"It's not so much about BEING funny as it is about SEEING funny."

~ Karyn Buxman
neurohumorist

Table of Contents

Foreword

by Kathleen B. Gaberson, PhD, RN, CNOR, CNE, ANEF

There are two kinds of nurses: OR nurses and those who wish they were. Karyn Buxman is not currently an OR nurse, but when you read this book, you will realize that she really "gets us." And now that she has written *What's So Funny About . . . OR Nursing?,* I'm sure she wishes she still *was* an OR nurse.

Most lay people would say that there is nothing funny about an operating room or the experience of surgery, despite being regular viewers of popular television series that depict outrageously comic antics of surgeons, nurses, and patients. For most patients, surgery is so scary that they just want to close their eyes, take a deep breath, and wish that they were somewhere else. (Oh, wait—that's why we give them sedation and general anesthesia! That explains everything!) Many OR nurses have days like that, too, when the stress of working in a high-pressure, high-stakes environment makes us wish that we could close our eyes and go to our Happy Place. But we can't steal a little of the IV sedation or the anesthesia gases for ourselves, so that we can tune-out and wake-up when it's all over. That's where the use of humor as a tactic to relieve stress, celebrate our nursing specialty, and accomplish our clinical, teaching, and management tasks more effectively comes in.

I've been an OR nurse for a very long time. I remember glass syringes; real woven cotton surgical drapes; scrub dresses and masks; re-usable cloth laparotomy sponges; re-processing surgical gloves; and suture that had to be threaded onto needles before being passed to the surgeon. But my funny stories about the Good Olde Days of OR nursing don't hold a candle to the absurdities of contemporary perioperative nursing practice. We use robots to perform prostate cancer surgery now, for heaven's sake—what could be more ludicrous than that? And as the size and complexity of the surgical team increases because of new roles (e.g., surgical technologists, RN first assistants, perfusion technologists, healthcare industry representatives), we have many more opportunities to find humor in the rich mix of personalities, expectations and perceptions.

So, sit back, relax, and enjoy reading Karyn Buxman's latest book in the *What's So Funny About…?* series. It will keep you in stitches (a little OR humor, there). May it lift your spirits and help to renew your commitment to providing safe, effective nursing care with optimal outcomes to a vulnerable patient population. Have fun, and learn a few new techniques to help you take yourself lightly while taking your work seriously. The OR will be a much kinder and gentler place for everyone when you do.

Kathleen B. Gaberson, PhD, RN, CNOR, CNE, ANEF *
PhD: Doctor of Philosophy, or, as some view it, Piled Higher and Deeper
RN: Registered Nurse, to be differentiated from the unregistered variety
CNOR: Certification that validates professional achievement of identified standards of practice by an RN providing care for patients before, during and after surgery
CNE: Certified Nurse Educator
ANEF: Fellow of the Academy of Nursing Education
* (If I can just get one more credential, I'll have more letters *after* my name than *in* my name.)

Acknowledgments & Dedications

OR nurses: This book is for *you.* I count the years I spent as an OR nurse as some of the finest (and funniest!) in my career. Talk about the tight bond among nurses! I learned true caring, compassion, and grace-under-pressure from my colleagues behind those double doors.

The work you do each and every day is making a tremendous difference. I salute you! I especially want to thank my OR Nurse pals Veronica Thomas, Nancy Roberts, Corinne Fessenden, and Lorie Khorsand for their extra input and support—you gals are awesome!

Here's a high-five to my colleagues, mentors and friends at the Association for Applied & Therapeutic Humor. We are making the world a better place one laugh at a time. And a special shout-out to Mary Kay Morrison and the Humor Academy for giving me the shove I needed to get this project into high gear.

Kudos to Dr. Lee Berk, Dr. Michael Miller, Dr. William Fry, and the many others who have conducted the clinical research behind this book. You are making a tremendous difference in the lives of people around the planet.

Thanks to my grad school (Go Mizzou!) advisors, Virginia Bzdek, Mandy Manderino, and Sherry Mustapha. You believed in me and encouraged me to take that first step—so many years ago—in spite of the fact that most everyone else saw research into therapeutic humor as "not professional enough." Your support has been like a pebble cast into the water. I really want you to know that your influence is now global in scope.

To Peter and all the regulars at the Pacific Bean Coffee Shop: Thanks for keeping me well-caffeinated during this book project. I haven't drunk that much coffee since I worked in surgery!

To my colleague-turned-beloved-friend Doug Fletcher, the original publisher of the hilarous (and infamous) *Journal of Nursing Jocularity* back in the 1990s; and to Dr. Vera Robinson, who, because of her pioneering work in therapeutic humor back in the 1970s, was lovingly referred to as the "Fairy Godmother of Humor."

To my advisor-and-buddy Sally and her terrific crew at Poole Communications: Thanks for making this book—and me!—look good.

A huge thank you to my editor Cindy Potts, whose talent, tenacity, and twisted sense of humor have made this entire "What's So Funny About" project a blast!

And, of course, this book would not be here were it not for my mildly-brilliant-and-oh-so-romantic-husband, Greg Godek. ["Who has more fun than you and me?" "Nobody!"]

Preface

Isn't OR nursing great? There's no question that becoming a nurse changes you . . . and being a nurse for five, ten, fifteen years (or longer!) changes you even more. One thing I've learned, from my own personal experience and from talking to hundreds of OR nurses just like you at association conferences and meetings, is that being an OR nurse changes you even *more* than that—in ways good and bad, heartbreaking and hysterical.

It's *one* thing to treat the ailment; it's quite *another* thing to treat the patient—the *person.* Treating the ailment requires *one* set of skills; while treating the person requires a *different* set of skills. The best nurses have mastered *both* sets of skills.

Etched into my brain is the curious-yet-common experience (for nurses, anyway) of the jarring juxtaposition of the clinical/medical facts, with the human/personal realities of patient care. I remember one of my very first days as a circulating nurse. The surgeon was performing an ATK amputation. Everything went well—right up until the point when I was carrying the severed limb away from the operating table . . . and the knee, as knees are wont to do, bent. At a moment like this, everything you learned about professional detachment and clinical distance goes right out the window—or at least it did for me! It becomes very, very real—the intense, intimately human side of OR nursing.

The human side—our patients: We see them when they're sleeping, and we know when they're awake—just like Santa Claus; except *our* presents arrive on a gurney, not a sleigh. And packages get delivered wrapped in gauze and a set of orders for Oxycontin and bed rest!

Patients amaze me. They come to us at some of the worst points in their lives. They're scared. They're overwhelmed. They're not sure what is going to happen. To see time and again that someone is capable of taking that fear and uncertainty and put it aside, trusting in the skill and compassion of the OR team—it's a powerful and humbling thing. Sure, for us, it's Wednesday morning at work. For them, it's their whole life.

And okay, maybe the patients aren't all that trusting . . . Raise your hand if you've ever found a patient who wrote "DON'T CUT THIS OFF!" on themselves in inch-high black Sharpie letters. Raise your other hand if you're thinking, "Hey, I'd do that, too!" [Touchdown!]

As OR nurses, we may be isolated from the rest of the hospital environment—but we're right on the front lines of patient care. There's so much we encounter, from the most serious to the sublimely silly. It is an amazing experience to be an OR nurse—and an amusing one as well. I've never met an OR nurse who didn't have some great funny stories. As a profession, we're adept at using humor to help manage the stress and tension of our daily lives.

Of course, we may be good at using humor because we've got so much fabulous material to work with! [But we'll be talking about the surgeons later on. Ha!]

So . . . Let's get this party started!

Introduction

It's no secret that I think nurses are amazing—it's really sort of blindingly obvious, actually—but OR nurses are a special kind of amazing. There is no such thing as a routine day when you're an OR nurse. You've got to be able to think on your feet, recognize and respond to potential complications, and advocate for the patient—all while providing the best possible care and maintaining a positive relationship with your OR colleagues.

No problem, right? Especially for eight-to-twelve hours at a go, day-after-day, week-after-week, year-after-year . . . we do it, because this is what we do. We're OR nurses.

"It would not be possible to praise nurses too highly."

~ Stephen Ambrose

OR nursing is an amazing profession, and OR nurses are amazing people. But let's not kid ourselves. This is demanding, tough work we're doing. There are tremendous demands on our physical, mental, and emotional resources. We need support.

Support isn't always forthcoming. The healthcare system is under increasing pressure to do more-and-more with less-and-less. Budgets are tight. Good leadership teams—teams that want to provide their nurses with every available resource to enhance morale and boost performance—simply don't have the money to make it happen.

That's why humor is so important. Laughter is an amazing therapeutic tool for you, your patients, and the OR team you work with. There are physical, emotional, and organizational benefits associated with the use of humor—and best of all, it's free! The purposeful and deliberate cultivation of humor in the OR is one way to ensure better patient outcomes, enhance individual professional performance, and boost team morale.

You don't need to spend any money to access humor. You don't need to buy anything to laugh. [It helps, of course, to buy this book. Ha! Multiple copies help even *more*, because then you can share the laughs with a friend!] In an environment of increased demands and dwindling resources, humor is the answer.

You may be thinking to yourself, "But I'm not funny. Can you teach me to be funny?" Well, yes. I could teach you a short comedy bit that might serve you every now and then. But it's not about *being* funny as much as it is about *seeing* funny. If you can "*see* funny," then the "*be* funny" will fall into place.

Odds are that you already have a sense of humor. The fact that you've picked up and are reading this book means that the chances are even better that it's a *good* sense of humor. But it's possible to improve and focus your humor skills to make them stronger and more effective. That way, when you really need a good laugh, you'll be able to have one—guaranteed!

So fasten your seatbelt, put your tray in the upright and locked position, and let's go!

Yours in laughter!
Karyn Buxman, RN, MSN, CSP, CPAE, neurohumorist

RN: Registered Nurse

MSN: Masters Degree in Mental Health Nursing

CSP: Certified Speaking Professional

CPAE: The Speaker Hall of Fame (the Oscars of the speaking profession)

Neurohumorist: One who combines applied humor with cutting-edge neuroscience

THIS BOOK IS INTENDED FOR OR NURSES ONLY.
ALTHOUGH 99.9% OF THE HUMOR CONTAINED
HEREIN IS BOTH UNDERSTANDABLE AND APPROPRIATE
FOR THE REASONABLY-INTELLLIGENT AND
LIBERAL-MINDED LAYPERSON—
IT'S THE REMAINING 0.1% OF THE CONTENT THAT
MAY CAUSE NON-PROFESSIONALS TO EXPERIENCE
HEART PALPITATIONS, DIZZINESS AND/OR
MORAL OUTRAGE.
THUS, THE READER MAY WANT TO CARRY THIS BOOK
IN A BROWN PAPER WRAPPER.

"Humor restores the human touch—
the caring— to the highly technical,
potentially dehumanizing world of healthcare."

~ Vera Robinson, RN, PhD

Chapter 1

What's NOT So Funny About OR Nursing?

Being an OR nurse is hard work. Let's talk about that for a moment. It's a conversation that doesn't happen as often as it needs to. OR nursing has its own distinct culture—which has its positives and its negatives. You can't beat the OR nursing culture for the closeness of team members. Working long hours in a demanding environment creates some of the strongest bonds in healthcare.

On the down side, there's this weird bravado that permeates the specialty. We give challenges the silent treatment—we just don't discuss the things that really bother us. One of the things we don't talk about is what OR nursing does to nurses.

Being a front line healthcare provider is tough work. You're the ultimate patient advocate—many times, for a patient who is completely unconscious and in no position to look out for himself or herself. Keeping things safe and moving requires the highest order of multi-tasking; your intense focus is required on multiple fronts. The sheer breadth of knowledge it takes to do your job is staggering. All of this takes a physical and emotional toll.

What is this doing to *you*?

As an OR nurse, you're under a lot of stress. OR nursing isn't the most stressful profession in the world—that "honor" clearly belongs to air traffic controllers. But OR nursing is pretty near the top of the list. You may not feel this stress all of the time—one of the great things about human nature is that we can acclimate ourselves to even the most outrageous of situations—but the stress has a real and dramatic impact on your physical and emotional health.

Laughter lightens one's mood.

Humor supports intimacy.

Frivolity reduces fear.

Here are some of the highlights:

- Heart health: Cardiovascular disease and hypertension are both linked to high stress levels. Heart disease is currently the number one cause of death in America, affecting nearly 50% of the population. How many bypass procedures go through *your* OR? In a significant percentage of those cases, stress was a precipitating factor.

- Respiratory health: People who have high levels of stress experience COPD and asthma more often than people who report lower stress levels.

- Digestive tract: Stress can work havoc on the GI system. Whether it's ulcers, gastritis, ulcerative colitis or IBS, stress can really make your stomach hurt. GI complaints are one of the most common stress-related conditions. Over the past two decades, we've seen procedures on the GI tract become steadily more and more common—surely a sign of our stressful times.

- Body aches and pains: High stress levels contribute to pain throughout the body, especially in the shoulders, neck, and lower back. For some people, lots of stress means they experience painful twinges, twitches, or ticks. Nurses have a high incidence of temporal mandibular joint disease—or

TMJ—from grinding and/or clenching their teeth. [Who? Me?!]

- Reproductive issues: Stress can really interfere with your love life—and any plans you may have for a future family. Research has tied high stress levels to impotence and infertility, as well as menstrual disorders and recurrent vaginal infections.

- Hair loss: Stress can make you go bald! —Or lose handfuls of your hair. [So much for a good hair day!]

Stress isn't good for our mental health, either. Anxiety, depression, irritability and insomnia are often reported by people experiencing high levels of stress. High stress levels can also manifest in aggressive, anti-social behavior. You only have to see one surgeon throw an instrument tray to realize how aggressive things can get in the OR. That's why it is important to find effective ways to continually manage stress.

And just to top things off, some research suggests that stress even make us get older faster! [We're not talking laugh lines here!]

"Wrinkles should merely indicate where smiles have been."

~ Mark Twain

I have to admit that being stressed-out isn't particularly fun or humorous. There's no point in making light of the serious side of our challenging profession. But while the *stress* that comes with OR nursing really isn't funny, the *experiences* you have while being an OR nurse can be absolutely hysterical.

The premise of this book—borne out by scientific research—is that humor has many practical benefits that OR nurses can use to benefit themselves, their patients and the team of professionals they're such a vital part of. Techniques of applied humor have made a positive difference in operating rooms across the country. It's easy, and it's fun.

So let's get going!

"If we took what we now know about laughter and bottled it, it would require FDA approval."

~ Dr. Lee Berk, researcher, psychoneuroimmunologist

Chapter 2
What Humor Can Do for You

Now some *good* news! Scientists are finally proving what most people have known since Biblical times: "A merry heart doeth good like a medicine." (Proverbs 17:22)

In Medieval times it was thought that if the body's fluids (known as "umors") were in balance, one was of good temperament—or healthy. That's where the phrase "having a good sense of humor" came from. The umors were yellow bile, blood, lymph, and black bile.

Throughout the Middle Ages, the practice of medicine was more art than science, and the mysterious art stagnated for many centuries. The following is from a *Saturday Night Live* skit, with comedian Steve Martin playing Theodoric of York, a doctor/barber:

"You know, medicine is not an exact science,
but we are learning all the time.
Why, just fifty years ago, they thought a disease
like your daughter's
was caused by demonic possession or witchcraft.
But nowadays we know that Isabelle is suffering from an
imbalance of bodily humors,
perhaps caused by a toad or a small dwarf
living in her stomach."

We now know that umor, or humor, isn't a body fluid at all. [Although as a nurse, chances are you know some very, very funny stories about body fluids!]

But believe-it-or-not, scholars still can't agree on a single, simple definition of just what humor really is! Some of the things they *do* agree on include: Humor is a mindset, a perspective, and something that tends to make you laugh. I know that seems obvious to you and me; but a researcher who is trying to analyze the effects of humor in a scientific manner needs to know exactly what he or she is measuring. They can't go by the Supreme Court standard ("I know it when I see it.").

Many years ago, while I was writing my thesis on the relationship between humor, health, and communication, I discovered that few "experts" could agree upon what humor really is.

One definition that has served me well over the years comes from my colleague, Dr. Joel Goodman, founder of The HUMORProject, who said, "Humor is a childlike perspective in an otherwise serious adult reality."

Most of us love the idea of looking at life through the eyes of a child—they have such a sense of fun and playfulness. It seems as if we lose the ability to view the world this way as we get older. Or if not the *ability*, then the *time* . . . There's so much to do, and our work is, quite literally, a matter of life or death. But rest assured: In reality, we have not lost our ability to play. We've simply forgotten what it looks like. The ability to see the world as a child *can* be recovered. You *can* tap back into the magic. It's just a question of changing perspectives.

Humor boosts morale.

Humor makes people more pleasant.

Humor helps when things go wrong.

Perspective is the underpinning of our ability to "reframe," our ability to *see* funny, and ultimately, our ability to just be happier.

> It was eight o'clock on a Monday morning. In my haste to get myself ready for the work day, I'd temporarily forgotten about my seven-year-old son. A rhythmic thumping noise coming from upstairs brought him back to mind.
>
> A mom-on-a-mission, I ran up the stairs. As I approached Adam's room I could feel the "Whomp! Whomp! Whomp!" vibrating through the walls.
>
> "What in the world—?!" I wondered.
>
> I opened his door and saw Adam—wearing nothing but his underwear and a big smile . . . jumping up and down on his bed . . . singing and dancing. . . swinging his shirt over and around his head . . . with enthusiastic kicks accenting the beat.
>
> *"What do you think you're doing, young man?"* I demanded.
>
> Adam stopped mid-jump, grinned a huge grin, and with the wisdom of Yoda, said, "Don't-ya-think-getting-dressed-in-the-morning-oughta-be-more-fun, Mom?!"

Humor is definitely a bit of a paradox. [Not to be confused with a pair-of-ducks!]

Humor can come from surprise. And surprises can make an OR nurse nervous. After all, surprises aren't always happy things. Yet much of humor is borne out of moments that made us uncomfortable—the way OR surprises sometimes can.

Humor can come from "derailment"—that sudden twist that makes a good joke work so well. Humor can also come from pure delight (watch young children for example; older folks don't experience nearly as much pure delight in living and discovering the world around them). And, believe it or not, sometimes humor and laughter can come from pain and suffering (see: banana peel; or most practial jokes; or Wiley Coyote dropping an anvil on his own head, in the pursuit of the Road Runner).

How important is humor? Consider this:

"A person without a sense of humor is like a wagon without springs. It's jolted by every pebble on the road."

~ Henry Ward Beecher

Humor plays a critical role in facilitating the physical and emotional resiliency that's so vital for anyone who is going to perform well in a high stress environment. There has been a lot of serious research into what *makes* us laugh, and what laughter *does* for us.

These studies come from part of a bigger field of research called psychoneuroimmunology (psycho: mind; neuro: nervous system; immunology: immune system) or sometimes referred to as the mind-body connection. Some experts throw in the endocrine system, too: psychoneuroimmunoendocrinology. [I'm pretty sure these scientists are just determined to win at Scrabble at all costs!] We'll refer to this field and research as PNI from here on out.

Here are the highlights of that research:

What Humor Can Do for Your *Body*

Humor and laughter have many positive effects on your body. PNI has illuminated many of the strong connections between the experience of laughter and improved wellness. Research has been conducted on the humor-health connection as it pertains to almost every body system: The cardiovascular, respiratory, and immune systems have been the primary focus, of course, and the work done there has been revelatory.

Let's Get to The Heart of The Matter

Humor can help you bring your cholesterol levels down—and it's way more fun than eating bowl after bowl after bowl of oatmeal! In a study conducted by psychoneuroimmunologist Dr. Lee Berk, and his endocrinologist and diabetes specialist colleague, Dr. Stanley Tan, participants spent half an hour a day watching movies or sitcoms that they found humorous. As a result, the participants' levels of HDL increased by 26%, while harmful C-reactive proteins declined by 66%.

When was the last time you heard that watching TV could actually make you healthier?! Another way you can really give your heart a boost is by playing the ICU Game: Any time you see an error on a medical TV show (*House* and *Grey's Anatomy* are GREAT for this!) that would result in the patient spending the rest of his short, short life in the ICU, get up and do 25 jumping jacks. You could have the heart of an Olympian in less than a season!

> **"Humor is a childlike perspective in an otherwise serious adult reality."**
>
> **~ Dr. Joel Goodman**

While you do want to reduce your harmful cholesterol, and lower your risk for cardiovascular disease, you probably don't want to do two-dozen jumping jacks between every set of commercials! Laughing is a lot less work. Reducing cholesterol is one example of how humor can do more than make you *feel* better: Humor can help you *be* better.

"The old saying that 'laughter is the best medicine,' definitely appears to be true when it comes to protecting your heart," says Michael Miller, M.D., Director of the Center for Preventive Cardiology at the University of Maryland Medical Center and a professor of medicine at the University of Maryland School of Medicine. *"The ability to laugh—either naturally or as a learned behavior—may have important implications in societies such as the U.S. where heart disease remains the number one killer... We know that exercising, eating foods low in saturated fat, and not smoking will reduce the risk of heart disease. Perhaps regular, hearty laughter should be added to the list."*

Improve Your Vascular Health

Laughter helps lower your blood pressure and increase circulation. Maintaining optimal circulation is absolutely critical. It's important for you to keep the blood moving to your extremities, flowing to your fingers and toes. Circulation is important because a constant, fresh supply of oxygenated blood keeps your energy level up—and if there's one thing every OR nurse needs, it's lots of energy!

One of the latest and most significant developments in PNI is a study by Dr. Miller. His research shows for the first time that laughter is linked to the healthy functioning of blood vessels. Laughter appears to cause the tissue that forms the inner lining of blood vessels, the endothelium, to dilate in order to increase blood flow.

"We know it works!" Dr. Miller told me. There's an apparent relationship between mental stress and vasoconstriction. And no one appreciates healthy circulation like an OR nurse does! We don't want our blood vessels tight and constricted. Nothing makes us happier than for them to be wide open, flexible healthy highways for the transport of oxygenated blood. "The endothelium is one of the most basic cardiac mechanisms. The fact that it is highly responsive to robust laughter means we have a real story here. And there's no downside to laughter!" adds Dr. Miller.

Blood Glucose Control

"Why should I worry about blood sugar? I don't have diabetes!" But did you know that 1 in 10 Americans has diabetes? The right lifestyle choices can help minimize that risk. And let's face it: When your lunch consists of a Diet Coke and a Snickers Bar, you're not making the world's best lifestyle choices.

So bring on the humor! Humor can help lower the increase in blood sugar you experience after eating a meal. A recent research study from Japan showed that people who watched a brief comedy show after eating, had lower glucose values than those who did not see the program. Pretty sweet!

Other studies show that laughing lowers your levels of the stress hormones cortisol and adrenaline. Cortisol increases insulin resistance, while adrenaline tells your liver to pump more glucose into your blood. The combined effect can be a lasting reduction in blood glucose levels. In other words, laughter can probably help lower your blood glucose *and* keep it down for quite a while!

"While there is no reason to expect humor to be helpful in preventing diabetes, it is helpful in managing it."

~ Dr. Paul McGhee,

Humor: The Lighter Path to Resilience & Health

Immune System

OR nurses have raised infection control to an art form. We'll preserve the integrity of a sterile field by any means necessary—and that's not Hollywood hyperbole. Protecting the patient is a top priority, but maintaining our own health in the face of some frightening emerging pathogens is a very, very close second. No one wants to wind up written into the medical literature, you know? That's why we take such elaborate, high-tech precautions in the OR.

Still, in the back of your mind, the worry remains. It doesn't have to be a huge pile of anxiety. It's just a little concern: "Is my own immune system strong enough to deal with what I face in the OR?"

Laughter is a low-tech way to augment your natural immune response. Humor and laughter have been found to significantly increase spontaneous lymphocyte blastogenesis, a natural killer cell activity, as well as stimulate Immunoglobulin A, which is especially helpful in combatting respiratory infections. Knowing this can reduce infection-related worry, thus lowering overall stress levels.

Gastrointestinal System

Remember back in nursing school when we learned that walking and moving patients around would improve peristalsis? Well, laughing can do the same thing. Our abdominal muscles massage our internal organs when we have a good belly laugh, which stimulates peristalsis and enhances digestion. This is good for us, and it can be good for patients who may not have the immediate ability to ambulate post-op.

"A person who belly-laughs doesn't bellyache."

~ Susan Thurman, English teacher

In a perfect world, all OR nurses would eat healthy meals, at reasonable intervals, at times roughly in alignment with the rest of humanity. It turns out that we don't necessarily live in a perfect world. I don't mean to shock you, but some OR nurses don't always eat the healthiest meals. In other words, no, you can't find all four food groups in the vending machine. [And grape-flavored bubble gum does *not* count as a fruit!] Meals are eaten on the go, at strange hours—or are sometimes skipped entirely. This can create havoc on your GI system.

Humor can help. Not as much as a well-timed ham sandwich, perhaps! Yet, I've found that the ability to access laughter quickly can be a tremendous asset when your stomach growls with the ferocity of a starving lion—especially when it coincides with the arrival of the surveyor from JCAHO!

Pain Management

Researchers have found that humor helps with pain management by increasing pain tolerance levels and by distraction. Chronic neck, back, and joint pain are part of too many OR nurses' lives. Knee, ankle and hip complaints are common as well. Whether the pain is sporadic or chronic, experiencing it adds an unwanted toll to your already full day. Effective pain management really should be part of your daily routine.

Laughter lowers blood pressure and reduces anxiety and inflammation. This helps relieve pain throughout the body. [Pain *outside* your body is beyond my scope of practice—sorry! Humor seems to be of little help in fighting politics or global warming.]

The Ohio State University Medical Center provides patients with a handout detailing the value of humor in pain management. By providing a distraction, humor shifts one's focus away from the pain and onto whatever you're laughing at. It doesn't *eliminate* the pain, but it helps you *deal with it* more effectively. Humor reduces the prominent position pain plays in your day.

Humor rewards and recognizes.

Humor levels social hierarchies.

Humor encourages openness.

What Humor Can Do for Your *Emotions*

Being an OR nurse requires you to have exceptional emotional elasticity. You're deeply invested in your patient, focused on achieving the best possible outcome—every time.

Some days are good days. Some days are bad days. You know what a bad day feels like. You know you went to work the next day after that bad day. That takes strength and fortitude. It takes what scientists call emotional resiliency—the ability to "bounce back" to a centered, stable emotional state relatively quickly after a shock or disruption of expected events.

Humor makes it easier to maintain your emotional stability and well-being while enabling you to provide the best possible patient care. Humor makes you feel good. It lifts the mood and results in a more positive overall outlook. That positive outlook is a great resource to have when you've just been chewed-up and spit-out by an uptight surgeon or an upset family member. But that's not all that humor can do. Humor also delivers the following valuable emotional benefits.

Provides an Outlet for Anger

Life is not fair, and if you want to see that proven, spend 24 hours in any operating room in the country. Bad things happen, and this makes us angry—angry at the causes of the bad things, angry that bad things happen at all, angry at the world where the bad things have become all too common. There are times when anger is an appropriate and even healthy response. But it's hard to be a good nurse while you're angry. The OR environment demands a clarity of thought inconsistent with intense anger. If you're so angry you can't see straight—that's not a good thing in the OR.

Anger accumulates. Anger builds. We collect our anger, sometimes consciously and sometimes not, and it accumulates. Resentment by resentment, anger grows and festers like a zit on our psyche. Look out when that thing pops . . . it's not going to be pretty.

Humor cures the infection of anger. Laughter is a very effective mechanism for processing negative emotions. Even the most bitter laughter is a form of gaining a new perspective on a situation. Many comedians assert that their best material comes out of the times in their lives when they were angriest. [I did not ask Jon Stewart. I assume *his* best material comes out of Washington!] And while people will run like the building is on fire when a complainer approaches, humor can be a socially acceptable—even enjoyable—way for people to vent.

"It is impossible for you to be angry and laugh at the same time. Anger and laughter are mutually exclusive and you have the power to choose either."

~ Wayne Dyer

Humor provides a way for us to express our anger, rather than repressing it. Try as we might, it's impossible to ignore these feelings over the long term. Add to that the fact that other people around you, whom you spend hours with every day, are having their own experiences with anger, and it can be a recipe for disaster. It's important to acknowledge that we have, at times, feelings of frustration and rage.

But we can't always *act* on our feelings of frustration and rage. There are laws against that type of thing! And doing nothing about it isn't really a good option. Repressed anger and frustration can make your stress levels skyrocket. Humor redirects anger, instead of avoiding or denying it. This redirection can defuse a lot of rage, bringing with it a sense of calm, relief and a fresh perspective. The underlying circumstances that made us angry still exist, but after we've laughed we're better prepared to address those circumstances.

It feels good to laugh at problems, if only for a moment. This doesn't mean closing our eyes to reality. Instead, laughter allows us to reframe the issue and look at it anew. Sometimes a change in perspective presents the information we need to move past the anger.

"Laughter gives us distance. It allows us to step back from an event, deal with it, and then move on."

~ Bob Newhart

Reduces Stress

Humor is a powerful tool for stress reduction. As we talked about earlier, stress is the biggest challenge associated with OR nursing. Stress has all kinds of negative physical and emotional ramifications that are better off avoided. For that reason, we need to minimize our stress levels.

Signs of Stress (The OR Nurse's Version)

- Everyone around you has an attitude problem.
- Every time you see an empty gurney you have an overwhelming desire to lie down on it.
- When you see an episode of *Scrubs*, your reaction is, "What's so funny about *that?!?*"
- When you see an episode of *Dexter*, your reaction is, "That's my life . . . Except with less blood."
- You feel like the author of the book *I've Got One Nerve Left and You're Standing On It.*
- You ate a one-pound bag of M&Ms at one sitting.
- You add chocolate chips to your Caesar salad.
- You swipe candy from patients' bedside tables while they're sleeping.

Is humor the *best* coping mechanism? It's certainly one of the *healthiest.* You can get over a bad day at work with a bottle of red wine—or two!—but that takes a toll on your system. Comfort eating, retail therapy, and behavior-based addictions like gambling, may feel good temporarily. In the long run, however, you might not be so thrilled with how things turn out. Laughter lets you have lots of fun—and you'll still be thin, sober and solvent in the morning.

By relieving anxiety and tension, humor provides a healthy escape from reality, and lightens the heaviness related to those aspects of caregiving that really weigh you down.

What Humor Can Do for You *Socially*

One of my favorite things about being a nurse, a humorist, and a professional speaker is the time I get to spend with OR nurses. It's my honor and privilege to hear about your triumphs, funny moments, and the challenges you face.

There's one challenge that keeps cropping up. Nurses, especially OR nurses, can be extremely lonely. Feelings of isolation often lead to depression and anxiety—not a good combination.

There are several reasons for this sense of isolation. One is the simply the nature of the job. We're busy every single minute of the day—surgeries are often scheduled long before the sun comes up, and on a bad day they can continue into the evening. How many times have you walked out of the OR surprised by how dark—or bright!—it is outside? Time flies when you're in surgery. There's simply no time to do anything *but* focus on the job at hand. Everyone you work with is busy too, which makes a tough situation even tougher.

Another reason OR nurses feel alone is that they *are* alone. OR teams tend to be self-contained units. There's typically not as much mingling or socialization between surgical teams and the rest of the hospital. Schedules may be dramatically different. OR teams tend to develop their own culture, complete with inside humor. Small, tight groups are nice, but they're also self-limiting. There are only so many people you know, talk with, and engage with on a daily basis. It can be isolating.

And . . . [Shhh!] [Don't tell anyone, but . . .] [Truth be told, there may be times when you wish you *were* alone!] [How many times have you gone to a family gathering or community event only to have someone discover that you're a nurse, and then spend the next half hour trying to get you to diagnose her mysterious rash in the shape of Antarctica, located on the small of her back—and she pulls-up her blouse to allow you to get a better view, and . . . well, you've been there. You don't need to have this experience many times before you start telling people that you're a life insurance salesman!]

"Laughter is the shortest distance between two people."

~ Victor Borge

Humor has been found to strengthen existing relationships (which is good if you *like* the people you know!). Regular use of humor is thought to make us more attractive to other people, which can increase your social circle and your base of support (and *this* is good news if you *don't* like the people you currently know).

In the next section, we're going to take a look at how that works.

Levels the Playing Field

As OR nurses, we occupy a unique place in the healthcare community. We're not surgeons—the folks who generally get all the credit. Our role is both vital and largely behind-the-scenes. This can make it difficult at times to form positive relationships with the other people we work with. Humor can help smooth over those differences.

A little humor helps to break down awkward moments between people. It doesn't matter what race you are, what gender or what religion you are, or how much money you make. If something's funny, people laugh.

Laughter reduces social hierarchies, making it easier for people from all different types of life circumstances to connect with each other. Whether it's surgeon/nurse, administrator/staff, or nurse/patient, when we can laugh together, communication becomes easier. And that's important.

What Humor Can Do for Your *Communications*

Gets Your Message Across

"The world goes around only by misunderstanding."

~ Charles Baudelaire

One of the top reasons that conflict occurs in the workplace is miscommunication. We *think* we're being clear. We assume that people are listening. And we believe that we are being understood. Ha!

> In the outpatient surgery clinic, many procedures are performed under local anesthetic. Some patients receive anesthesia with epinephrine, others don't. The surgeon, wanting to con-

> firm that the correct medication had been drawn up, turned to the circulating nurse and asked, "Epi?"
>
> She looked at him and said, "Yes, I'm happy—why wouldn't I be?"

Another important characteristic of humor is that it grabs people's attention. Teachers, preachers, speakers, and politicians all agree, if you want to get people listening, get them laughing. People enjoy laughing. And when you inject humor into your communications, people pay more attention and they loosen-up—which helps your serious messages to be heard more clearly.

> *Overheard in the OR:*
>
> *Nurse: "I'm ready. I have everything but the kitchen sink!"*
>
> *Surgeon: "I'd like the kitchen sink!"*

Humor can serve as a safety net for difficult conversations. The ability to frame topics as potentially humorous material allows you to bring up serious subjects while "testing the waters" with your audience. If they respond well to your humorous tone, it becomes easier to move the conversation forward and address larger issues. Even humor that doesn't *work* can spark meaningful, much-needed conversations. Even a joke that falls flat can be a door-opener. You might shrug your shoulders, chuckle and say, "I never *could* tell a joke. But you know, the issue of ______ *is* no joke!"

Humor can enhance important communication, whether it's with a patient, a colleague or a friend.

"Many a true word is spoken in jest."

~ ENGLISH PROVERB

Diffuses Difficult Situations

The OR is the setting for many difficult, tense moments. There are many ways to deal with difficult situations—but one that's frequently overlooked is humor.

"Language was created so we could communicate. Humor was created so we could complain."

~ KARYN BUXMAN, NEUROHUMORIST

When things get tense, whether it's dealing with a red-faced surgeon in a full-fledged-meltdown, or a garden-variety personality conflict, humor can diffuse the anger, relieve the tension, and level the playing field. Good communicators—like successful comedians or politicians (or comedians who *become* politicians; see: Al Franken)—will have a list of laugh lines, or "saver lines," that they can pull out when things unexpectedly go awry.

You never know when you're going need them, but if you can come up with your own saver lines, you can give yourself more power and control by being proactive. Try this: Collect humorous lines and quotes you can use to stop angry bluster in its tracks. If people start laughing, they stop yelling, and that's good news for everyone. Here are some saver lines you can use to get started:

- *"There can't be a crisis today—my schedule is already full."*
- *"If you are grouchy, irritable, or just plain mean, there will be a $10 fine for putting up with you."*
- *"Everyone brings me happiness . . . some by arriving, some by leaving."*
- *"Is it time for* YOUR *medication or* MINE*?"*

Last important point here: After using a humorous response, you should then address the problem at hand. The idea isn't to get the other person laughing so hard that you can escape unnoticed [although that might come in handy for some really desperate situations!]. You're just trying to decrease the tension at hand so leveler heads can prevail.

"Laughter is the most inexpensive and most effective wonder drug."

~ Bertrand Russell

Chapter 3
Humor: The Good, the Bad, and the Ugly

Laughing WITH or Laughing *AT*?

While the U.S. Constitution assures us that "all men are created equal," that venerated document is completely mute on the subject of humor. [John Adams didn't have much of a sense of humor. Apparently, he left that to Benjamin Franklin.]

The Bill of Rights, however, *does* provide for freedom of speech. And this, my fellow funny nurses, is just the opening we're looking for! The following is a paraphrasing of the First Amendment. [Disclaimer: Not intended as legal advice!]

Freedom of speech is the political right to communicate one's opinions and ideas. So this means that if, in a U.S. citizen's opinion, a knock-knock joke about cardiac surgeons is funny, then he or she is allowed to tell it. And, if—in, say, an OR nurse's opinion—this joke *(Q: How many doctors does it take to change a light bulb? A: Nobody knows. They all expect the nurses to do it!)* cracks-up the OR team, then we are allowed to tell/text/blog/share it!

Now, just because we are *allowed* to express humor, does not mean that all humor is appropriate, helpful, or healthy.

> ***Laughing provides a sense of control.***
>
> ***Humor helps people perservere.***
>
> ***Humor provides a safe space to process emotions.***

There are many types of humor, and some kinds of humor are healthier than others. Some kinds of humor make you feel good. And, there are other kinds of humor that can make you feel bad.

Take sarcasm for instance. Personally, I'm a real fan of sarcasm—and chances are that many of the people you work with are, too. In the right setting with the right people, it can be appreciated (see section below on Bond, Environment and Timing). However, some researchers have classified sarcasm as a form of aggressive behavior. It's easy for sarcasm to cross the line into bullying or abusive behavior. (The Greek origin of the word sarcasm, sarkasmós, means "to tear the flesh.") [Ouch!]

If you've ever been sniped with a sarcastic remark, you may feel like you were missing a bit of hide. There are a number of ways to respond to aggressive sarcasm, ranging from simply saying "Really??" to taking the commenter aside to let him or her know they're not all that funny. Ignoring remarks that bother you may *seem* like an effective coping strategy, but the truth is that sarcasm may lead to increased levels of anger and frustration. Establishing and maintaining boundaries regarding the types of humor people can use with you is a vital part of self-care.

Understanding the Types of Humor

Humor comes in a number of flavors. There's *constructive* humor—the light, upbeat type of humor that builds people up. (A side benefit is that it builds *you* up, too!) And then there's *destructive* humor, which is a more negative type of humor, where we find the laughs at other people's expense. Wise to avoid!

Which is which? If you would feel ashamed if someone you respect heard the joke, it's likely negative humor. If someone you didn't like told you the joke you were just telling, would you find yourself offended or incensed? Negative humor.

It's a matter of laughing genuinely *with* someone versus laughing *at* someone. It's always healthier to laugh *with* others than to laugh *at* them. Occasionally you may find yourself in the predicament of not being able to help yourself from laughing at someone. Here's a line that may keep you out of trouble: "I'm sorry that I'm laughing. It reminds me of the time I (fill-in-the- blank)." Now you've turned the laughter back on yourself instead of onto the other person. Generally a wise thing to do.

To build bonds and strengthen relationships in the OR, you want to practice humor that makes others feel safe. One technique that usually works well is self-deprecating humor—making fun of yourself. No one will be offended, and it will actually show people that your self-esteem is strong enough to withstand being teased. Self-deprecating humor can actually increase other people's opinion of you!

A Word (or 872) about "Sick Humor"

One kind of humor that falls into the gray zone is "sick humor." When tragedy and death cloud our lives, they darken our humor as well. Anyone who has to deal with issues that are tragic or unfair is a great candidate for sick humor (also known as dark humor, gallows humor, or black humor). Guess where OR nurses fall on this scale?? People who know first-hand the harsh realities of healthcare are among the world's biggest fans of sick humor. (Our colleagues in dealing first-hand with human tragedy and suffering include police officers, firefighters and soldiers. On behalf of your OR nurse cousins, I salute you!) That being said, I must confess that OR nurses are special fans of humor featuring body fluids, death and dismembership. [Please don't tell our mothers!]

"All bleeding stops . . . eventually."
~ Anonymous

Anyone who deals with traumatic situations is likely to count on some type of "sick humor" to help them keep their balance amid difficult situations. For example, police officers, fire fighters and soldiers all have their own styles of dark humor that helps them get by, and also bonds them to one another. It's a special brand of humor that is not meant for outsiders. And that makes sense, because if you've never experienced what *they* have, you're not really a member of their "tribe."

Any kind of humor that makes you laugh, whether it's sick or not, is going to relieve your stress. It may not, however, do much for the stress of the people around you! Those who share your pain and experiences as a nurse will "get it." Those who don't, won't. That's just the way it is.

Risky Business (and the B.E.T. Method)

Have you ever tried to be funny and put your foot in your mouth? [I certainly have!] There's almost always some degree of risk involved when you use humor. My purpose in sharing these insights is to help you push the cost/benefit ratio into the plus column. Here are three ways to take some of the risk out of the risky business of humor, and make your humor a safe B.E.T. (B stands for "Bond"; E stands for "Environment"; and T stands for "Timing.")

B = Bond

The Bond represents those areas where you have a point of commonality with the people you're about to share your humor with. Where are you connected? Are they work colleagues? Are they neighbors? High school pals? Drinking buddies? If you have a close relationship with your listeners, you'll definitely know what will make them laugh; but if your relationship is newer or more casual, then you won't be on such firm ground.

Use some common sense here. Consider the people you're with at the time. Are they the type of people who get offended easily? If so, you'll want to hold back on some types of humor. On the other hand, if you're with a bunch of George Carlin fans, you know that your humor can be sharper.

The longer you've known the people, and the better your relationship is with them, the safer your humor will be. If you've shared some gross-out humor with your long-time pal in the OR, she's probably going to overlook the ickiness, not be offended, and will likely laugh heartily. However, if it's someone you've known for only a short time (a patient, for instance), or have only known casually (the equipment rep who shows up once a year), you may want to edit some of your humor before sharing it with them.

E = Environment

Being aware of the environment also helps determine if humor is appropriate. There's a saying that, "There's a time and a place for everything," and environment is all about the place. As OR nurses, we have to make sure that our use of humor doesn't have a negative impact on the healthcare environment. This can be a fine balancing act: You want to use humor enough that the patients feel more relaxed, but not so much humor that they question your professionalism or skill.

Anyone who *hears* your humor, *sees* your humor, or *experiences* your humor is part of your audience, whether you mean for them to be or not. The patient who appears to be safely off in dreamland might actually be hearing every single word you say. An ounce of caution is worth an entire afternoon of explaining and apologizing!

T = Timing

You can have the right audience, in the right setting, and use humor—only to have it fall flat. Timing is perhaps the most difficult element to master when using humor. Have you ever heard people say, "Too soon!" to jokes about unfortunate events? They're not ready to laugh about the situation yet.

How can you tell if the timing is right? How much time must elapse before an event can be funny? To be able to laugh at a moment or experience, you need to be able to emotionally detach from it. It has to be possible to look at the set of circumstances without re-experiencing the emotional response you had when the event occurred.

That process of detaching can take time. It's not an instant process—nor should it be! As complete human beings, we experience a wide range of emotions in response to life events. Anger, frustration, upset, and embarrassment all have their role to play.

At the peak of a crisis things simply ain't that funny. But we learn from our life experienes (eventually!), and they help us grow.

After we've learned those lessons, it's time to laugh. Have you ever found yourself saying, "Someday I'm going to laugh about this"? One option that people rarely consider is to consciously choose to shorten that timeframe. It *is* possible!

Any OR accident or mishap has a lot of potential to be Very Not Funny. But *sometimes* there *is* laughter to be found, at least according to one OR Manager I know:

> "We'd been called in for an emergency bowel obstruction. Our scrub nurse had some bad gas—don't ever trust the cafeteria's tacos! In the middle of the procedure, the surgeon starts freaking out. 'I nicked the bowel! Do you smell that?' He ran the bowel over and over before he was finally satisfied that it was intact, and he closed. Afterward, when I talked to the scrub nurse about it, she said, 'What was I going to do?? Tell him I *farted?!*' "

Some people can distance themselves immediately. They can laugh at their own mistakes—whether it's driving out of the parking lot with a sack of groceries still on top of the car, or saying something dumb in a meeting.

But other people need more time to process their reactions and emotions. When some people make a mistake, they berate themselves harshly. And as long as they are emotionally attached to the painful event, they will not find it funny.

Neurobiologists have proven that humor provides benefits to the cardiovascular, respiratory, immune, and musulo-skeletal systems.

And then there are those folks who will just *never* see the situation as funny. And that's okay, too. None of us have the right to force our own coping style—or humor style—on anyone else.

Effective stress management involves practicing emotionally detaching from painful events, searching instead for the humor those moments contain. It isn't always easy, but with practice you'll find that you've developed the "Humor Habit."

When to Use Humor?

Sometimes it is difficult to tell whether humor is appropriate in a given situation. Many times, we're so worried about whether laughing is really the right thing to do at any particular moment, that we censor ourselves, stopping ourselves from using humor.

This is the "When in doubt, leave it out" approach. This is undoubtedly the *safest* option. Use it *too* often, however, and you may leave yourself unable to capitalize on some of the many benefits of humor.

It's also important to remember to refrain from using humor during moments of crisis, or when it's vitally important that communication be clear and concise. Humor often works by distracting the attention, and there are times when distraction is a Very Bad Idea.

Before using humor, do a quick mental "time-out":

- What is my *connection* with the audience?
- Is this the right *setting* for this type of humor?
- Is this the right *time* to use humor?

The Safest Form of Humor

When in doubt about what kind of humor to use with others, use self-effacing humor (making fun of yourself). Sharing a funny story about yourself shows self-confidence and yet also shows vulnerability. People find this kind of humor totally non-threatening and they may likely feel secure enough to share their own personal humor back with you.

Note 1: With self-effacing humor, it's best to focus on the funny or dumb thing that you *did*, and not on *yourself* as being a dumb person.

Note 2: Using self-effacing humor requires self-confidence, and a strong sense of who you really are.

"Laugh at your actions, not at who you are. It's safer to admit that you made a mistake than to admit that you are a mistake."

~ Terry Paulson, PhD

My friend and humor colleague Linda MacNeal refers to self-deprecating humor as "Human Humor," saying that she values the ability to laugh at the fact she's only human. This is a really healthy framework to use when we choose to poke fun at our own failings and foibles.

Remember this: You are *somebody*. Somebody who can be strong enough and confident enough to poke fun at yourself. Remember this, too: People who never use self-deprecating humor are not as confident and strong as they would like you to believe!

"I always wanted to be somebody . . . but I should have been more specific."

~ Lily Tomlin

That's a little tidbit to keep in mind while using humor. Self-deprecating humor is a strong and powerful technique to help you deal with a stressful career, not to mention your everyday life. The trick to self-deprecating humor is to make sure you focus on the things you *do*—and not the person you *are*.

Seriously. The world does enough to tear us down. We don't have to do it to ourselves.

"Once you find laughter,
no matter how painful your situation might
be, you can survive it."

~ Bill Cosby

Chapter 4
Laughter is the Best Medicine: Humor and Your Patients

If you think it's tough being an OR nurse, just try being a *patient* in that OR! The exercise of "standing in another person's shoes" is always enlightening.

99.9% of the time, the patients we see would rather be anywhere else on the planet. Not many people wake up in the morning saying, "Hurray! I get to have open heart surgery today!" Surgery is a scary prospect—and that's *before* you factor in any other personal or social stresses the patient might be experiencing. When *we* see people, they're not necessarily having their best day ever. [Understatement.]

Humor has a vital role to play in providing the best possible patient care. Laughter can help make the patient's time in the OR less stressful and overwhelming. Take for example Ed Gamble, a patient who pranked his recovery room nurse. As an adult male having to go in for a circumcision, he was determined that something *fun* should come out of the situation—so he came up with this practical joke: Ed's surgery required a general anesthetic. So, he secretly prepared by repeating a short phrase to himself over and over again, as the anethesia was administered. An hour and a half later, as he stirred in the recovery room, he looked up at his nurse, his unconscious mind took over, and he murmured, "Have they sorted out my cataracts yet?" While the nurse nearly had a heart attack, Ed gently fell back to sleep! (Full disclosure: Ed is an actual, for-real comedian. And you can see him on YouTube. Search for "Ed Gamble, hospital prank.") [Yes, Ed is a twisted man . . . I *like* that about him!]

Humor provides measurable physiological benefits.

Laughter relieves social tension.

Laughter relieves internal tension, too!

Not many patients are as proactive (and funny!) as Ed Gamble. This is where we OR nurses can step-in and utilize applied humor. Of course, it's impossible to remove *all* fear and anxiety from a surgery—the anesthetist has to have *something* to do!—but we can, with the strategic, therapeutic use of humor, significantly lower the stress levels a patient is experiencing. And this leads to better patient outcomes, which is good news for everyone.

It is in the pre- and post-op period when our patients are most likely to benefit from humor. (It's a scientific fact that it is a lot easier to laugh when you're *awake*—and a lot, *lot* easier to laugh when those nifty drugs are still working their way through your system!)

And now, for those of you who are taking notes . . . Here are eight ways you can use humor to benefit your patients:

(1) Decrease Fear by Increasing Frivolity

For optimal patient outcomes, we want our patients to come to us in a calm, centered emotional state. Ideally, they'll be fully informed about what's going to happen, including the benefits they'll get from the procedure, and some idea of what the healing process is going to be like. The patient should be free from anxiety, stress, and fear.

I don't know about you, but those weren't the

patients I saw in pre-op! Very few of us work in an ideal world. Our patients come to us more than a little anxious. Luckily, laughter has amazing stress-busting powers. Alleviating anxiety and fear requires a two-pronged approach. The first essential step is making sure that your patient really does understand what is going to happen. Discussing the procedure in layman's terms can put some of the fear to rest.

That was certainly true for one little boy . . .

> Five-year-old Bobby was being prepped to have his kidney removed. The kidney was going to his baby sister. The boy understood that Sally really, really needed the kidney in order for her to stay alive.
>
> But he still had one question for Nurse Martha. He asked her, "Will it hurt?"
>
> Nurse Martha patiently explained that he'd be asleep for the procedure, and that he wouldn't feel a thing.
>
> Bobby interrupted her, saying, "No! I mean, will it hurt when I die?"
>
> Martha was stunned, then she almost laughed. But she immediately shifted

into "kid-mode," and she understood where Bobby was coming from. The poor little fellow had no expectation of surviving the procedure! None of the adults—not even his loving parents—had looked at the situation through the eyes of a five-year-old. Here's the logic: If *baby Sally* was going to die without a working kidney, then *Bobby* would die if *his* kidney was removed. (Makes sense, doesn't it?) And here's the kicker: The little guy was willing to give up his life for his sister!

Nurse Martha assured Bobby that he definitely was *not* going to die; that he would merely sleep through the operation and not feel a thing; that he would recover quickly, and would be able to go home in only three days; and that he would be back outside playing in two weeks.

This cheered Bobby up—but not as much as you might expect. He pouted and said, "I guess this means I still gotta clean my room!"

[Whew! Okay, back to the adult world . . .]

Having your patients explain to you, in their own words, the procedure they're going to have, can be a source of mirth and delight for both of you. One older gentleman, awaiting an orchiectomy, proudly reported that the doctor was going to change him "from a rooster into a hen!"

These conversations can relieve some of the tension the patient is experiencing—and they can also open the door to larger conversations. That particular patient had some concerns about his future sex life that had been weighing heavily on his mind. Because he was able to laugh about the situation with the nurse first, he felt safe enough in the clinical environment to bring up his worries.

(2) Lower Patients' Stress Levels with Delight & Diversion

Murphy's Law for OR Nurses: "The more freaked out and afraid the patient is, the higher the likelihood that her procedure will be delayed for hours and hours and hours."

Anticipation is a powerful force. Dr. Lee Berk, a leading psychoneuroimmunologist, has conducted research that indicates looking forward to a fun event (laughing with friends, going to an amusement park, etc.) can have almost as many health benefits as enjoying the event itself. Negative anticipation (a state of being fearful in advance—dreading what is to come) has the opposite effect.

There is no environment on earth more prone to negative anticipation than the pre-op suite!

Put yourself in the patient's place: Once you're gowned-up and on a gurney, waiting to be wheeled through those double doors, there's not a whole lot you can do except *think*. You're lying there imagining what's to come . . . dwelling on what's about to happen, and the many ways it could all go wrong. This is not going to improve your mental outlook! Your imagination is likely to run amok creating all kinds of possible negative scenarios.

Re: Nature vs. Nurture: "Genetics loads the gun, and environment pulls the trigger."

~ Dr. Francis Collins

How might you help your patients combat that negative mindset? With delight and diversion, of course! These two humor strategies are powerful tools for countering pre-op negative anticipation. Humor delights and distracts people, and improves their mental outlook.

One way to create delight and diversion is to make the pre-op suite more patient-friendly. I have visited several facilities that have done a great job making that environment more cheerful and upbeat. Something as simple as a TV tuned to a funny program can provide much-needed distraction. Sitcoms or

America's Funniest Videos work well for this. One doesn't need to concentrate intently in order to get a laugh or two.

Another strategy is to encourage patients to distract themselves. As a nurse, you can provide this encouragement directly . . . "Just be careful how you do it!" says Veronica Thomas, RN, Director of Nursing for Northeast Missouri Ambulatory Surgery Center:

> "We discovered that our pediatric patients did much better if they had something *fun* to do while they were waiting for their procedure. So we got some handheld video games—Gameboys—for the kids to play with. They loved them. This was when Gameboys were fairly new and very cool.
>
> So early in the shift one of our OR nurses brings in a peds patient and gets him ready to go. Then, remembering our new protocol involving the Gameboy, she turnes to the little fellow and says, "While you're waiting, would you like me to get you a *Playboy*?" [Oops!]

(3) Listen Beyond the Laughter

Humor has many critical roles to play in the healing process. One of the most important occurs when patients use jokes and laughter as a way to address topics that they're not prepared to bring up directly. When patients are using humor, it's often a good sign that they're processing the many complex feelings that go along with having surgery. Listening *beyond* the laughter can be particularly revealing:

> "We had a little old lady coming in for a colectomy. She seemed like she was in great spirits, and laughed heartily when I discovered she'd written 'Don't cut this off!' in black magic marker on her left foot, with arrows pointing to each toe. She'd *also* marked her *right* foot, too—*and* both of her arms! Her laughter faded a bit when I asked her about it. 'Surgeons make mistakes,' she said quietly. 'I'm just trying to help them do a good job'." [Wow . . .]

This behavior is not uncommon. Uncertainty provokes anxiety, especially when that uncertainty is tied to our health and well-being. It's not easy to express that anxiety directly. Using humor—even dark, borderline, "inappropriate" humor—gives people a safe way to talk about things that are troubling them.

With this in mind, it's important that we learn to listen *beyond* the laughter. Of course, maintaining appropriate standards for the therapeutic environment is important, but we also have to focus on what's actually being communicated. When we do that, we create opportunities to identify those points of need and anxiety we can actually remedy. Sometimes it's a situation where conveying accurate information or clarifying medical terminology can provide tremendous peace of mind. In other instances, we may not have any answers—but we can still be there to listen and provide compassionate support.

(4) Equip Yourself for Life's Most Embarrassing Moments

I've done extensive research, delving deeply into the medical literature in order to confirm what nurses have long known: Embarrassment is *not*, in fact, a fatal condition.

Good luck trying to get your patients to believe that! Intellectually, they understand that the body has ways to eliminate the build-up of excess internal gas. They know the process is natural and they may even accept that it is necessary. But that intellectual knowledge pales against the feelings of humiliation, mortification, or plain old garden variety embarrassment that can come with passing gas where other people can hear (and smell!) it.

Some patients won't be bothered one little bit by passing gas. [Frankly, I've had some who have raised farting to a fine art!] The Recovery Room can be the source of a strange symphony, reminiscent of bassoonists warming up before a chamber concert, all of them almost entirely out of tune. There are people who will hear this happening all around them, and they will laugh and laugh and laugh.

There are other people—often from an older generation, a more reserved culture, or a particular gender—who find the entire experience mortifying. Novice nurses have been known to interpret the crimson flush on the necks, forehead and cheeks of these patients as a sign that something is very wrong. Let me be the first to assure you that the surgeon will not appreciate a call at home updating him on this particular change in patient condition. [Don't ask me how I know this.]

OR nurses can use humor to show these patients that they're not alone, while simultaneously modeling a more appropriate response to some of life stressors, perhaps by sharing our own embarrassing experiences. When one's face is red, it helps a lot to know that someone else has been in a similar situation—and survived the experience . . . *and* could laugh about it later!

Flatulence is not the only source of embarrassment in a healthcare setting! When I was teaching nursing, I loved to share this story about my experience working as a circulating nurse:

> One morning, while I was hurrying down the hallway to circulate for a C-section, I saw a tall, young man in scrubs looking somewhat lost. "Must be the soon-to-be father," I thought. Out loud I asked, "Are you looking for the C-section?" He nodded.
>
> "Well, you can't go into the operating room without a mask! Follow me." I took him by the elbow, and led him—gently-but-firmly—over to the scrub sink, where I showed him the proper way to wash his hands. I then handed him a mask. "You take these two strings and tie them like *this* . . ." I demonstrated, " . . . and you take *these* two strings and tie them—like *so!*"
>
> The man nodded slowly, then replied, "Thank you. But I prefer to tie mine like *this*." He then extended his hand to me. "I'm the new pediatrician, Dr. McHardy."

I smiled back, shook his hand enthusiastically, and said, "Welcome! I'm *Nancy Roberts*, the OR supervisor."

It was two weeks before he discovered that I'm *not* Nancy Roberts!"

[Never Let Them See You Sweat.]

(5) Get Them Laughing, Get Them Learning!

The Perioperative Outcomes Initiative examines every aspect of patient care to determine ways that it can be improved. Patient education plays a critical role in securing positive outcomes: Simply following the discharge instructions can make a huge difference in the patient's recovery.

Veronica Thomas, RN, recommends providing your post-op instructions during the pre-op phase. At that point, your patients are more alert, focused, and receptive to what you have to say. They're also more likely to remember what you tell them. The amnesiac effects of many anesthetics are powerful indeed, and even the best post-op instructions may be lost in the "fog"! Humor *also* has a role to play in the process.

This year, there will be approximately 53,000 tonsillectomies performed in the US. This means that there will be *more* than 53,000 times that patients will receive detailed instructions about the best way to conduct themselves in order to effect a speedy and complete recovery.

Let's be real here: These instructions aren't brain surgery [or even rocket science!]. "Don't pick up heavy objects, stick to clear fluids for a while, and monitor for fever or signs of infection." There's nothing on this list that should confuse anyone. This is simple stuff.

Yet I guarantee you that in an emergency room somewhere near you, a post-tonsillectomy patient is presenting, right this very minute, with excruciating pain. It will turn out, upon investigation, that Cool Ranch Doritos are not, in fact, a clear liquid.

How in the world does this happen?? What's going wrong here? Undergoing surgery can be scary and overwhelming. Patients who are anxious often develop a type of tunnel vision, where they can only see what they *need* to see in order to get out of the surgery center as quickly as possible. They're so focused on "getting out of Dodge," and back home, that any possible distraction—even something as helpful as patient education—becomes meaningless background noise to them.

This is where humor helps. Humor is a disruptive

force—[that's why the teacher doesn't love the Class Clown]—and this disruptive force can be harnessed to help our patients move from that single-minded focus of "I-want-to-go-home! I-want-to-go-home!" to a place where they can be open-to and aware-of the information they'll need to heal properly.

Let's say we're talking about recovery times. We can share the straight-forward facts, or, in those instances where it appears that the patient may not actually be paying attention, try using humor to get through. Here's a story that I've used in that situation:

> Two little boys were in a hospital, about to go in for surgery. The first boy asked the second, "What are you in here for?" The second boy said he was going to have his tonsils out. The first boy comforted the second, explaining that it wasn't so bad: "A bit of a sore throat, and lots of ice cream! And you'll be playing really soon!"
>
> The second boy then asked what his new buddy was in for. The first boy replied that he was getting circumcised. The second boy shook his head sadly and said, "Oh no! I had a circumcision when I was a baby, and I couldn't walk for a year!"

It takes most patients a moment to get it—and the "Ah-ha! moment" shifts their awareness. They start becoming more fully present in the moment, and that means more attention paid to post-op instructions—and, all things being equal, fewer Cool Ranch Doritos.

Humor is not a magic bullet. You won't get every patient to pay attention by making them laugh. But for the ones who *do* stop, and listen, and laugh, there's a greater chance they're going to remember and comply with post-op instructions. And that leads directly to better patient outcomes.

(6) Use High-Touch, Not Just High-Tech

Medicine is an art and a science—and it's often the *art* part that leaves even the best surgeons stymied. Humor can play a role in closing the communication gap that often crops up between the technically-expert, focused clinical team, and the very, very human patient.

> "Our patient satisfaction surveys had revealed that while our *standard of care* was excellent, patients felt the whole *process* was too mechanical and impersonal. They wanted more direct interaction with the physician. Specifically, they wanted the doctors to touch

them. It didn't matter if the doctor could determine everything that was wrong with them simply by reading their x-ray; there was something about physical contact that made them feel better cared-for.

"We tried to communicate this to one of our best orthopedic surgeons, not a touchy-feely kind of guy. He listened attentively, and said he'd try to do better. So in comes the next patient, a little old lady who needed surgery on her elbow. She's a fiesty gal, and a bit on the plump side.

"The doctor is reading the x-ray while reaching under the blanket and palpating the complaint area—when the gal looks him straight in the eye and says, 'Honey, I'm not going to stop you . . . but if you think that's my elbow, you're sadly mistaken!' "

(7) Empower Your Patients Thru Humor

Why are our patients anxious and stressed-out? Part of the reason is that going into surgery requires surrendering a significant amount of control—far more than we do at most other times in our lives. Wearing a revealing gown, being without one's phone or computer (often more stressful than the surgery itself!), or being on one's own without family or friends around can be an overwhelming experience.

One of the ways patients try to deal with this (and enjoy better outcomes) is by being vigilant about their care. They want to be informed. The more they know about what's going on, the more they feel in control of the situation.

Sometimes, this can lead to confusion—which is when a good sense of humor can be your best friend!

> A male patient is lying in bed in the hospital, wearing an oxygen mask over his mouth and nose, still heavily sedated from a four-hour surgical procedure.
>
> A student nurse arrives to give him a partial sponge bath.
>
> "Nurse," mumbles the man, from behind the mask, "Are my testicles black?"

Embarrassed, the young nurse replies, "I don't know, sir. I'm only here to wash your upper body."

The man mumbles again, "Nurse, are my testicles black?"

Concerned that something might really be wrong, or that he might elevate his vitals from worrying about his testicles, the student nurse overcomes her embarrassment and sheepishly pulls back the covers.

She raises his gown, examines him closely, and palpates his genitals.

She then says, "No sir, there's nothing wrong with you, and your testicles are not black."

The man shakes his head emphatically. He then reaches up, pulls off his oxygen mask, and slowly and deliberately enunciates, "Thank you very much, nurse. But what I was actually asking was . . . 'Are-my-test-results-back?'

[!!]

(8) Build Resiliency with Humor

> "Two days a month, an oral surgeon comes to our facility to serve patients who would have no other way to be seen. On those days, the place is packed. His patients are a mix of the chronically underserved: The very poor, the mentally ill, the elderly, the homeless and the forgotten.
>
> "It can make for a rough day. Frankly, some patients don't know how to behave in a clinical setting. It can be a circus!
>
> "These patients need our care and respect. But if things are going to be a circus, then so be it! As they say, if you can't beat' 'em, join 'em. We make the best of it—and we do a good job. On those days we snack on peanuts and popcorn. We're all expert jugglers—and we're really great at 'clowning' around."

It doesn't matter how long you've been working as an OR nurse, there are going to be patients that you just can't connect with. Nursing takes an emotional toll. When you see the same patients come in, time and time again, to have completely avoidable complications addressed, we experience frustration and tension. Working with patients who aren't as clean, or as well-mannered, or as well cared-for as we might like them to be, can be emotionally and spiritually draining.

"Humor by CHANCE can be beneficial, but humor by CHOICE creates amazing, life-changing results."

~ Karyn Buxman neurohumorist

Humor allows us to address those frustrations and tensions while providing the best possible patient care. One of the most valuable humor techniques, demonstrated above, is that of "reframing." Having a facility full of difficult patients can indeed be a circus—but there are *good* circuses and there are *bad* circuses. This team chose to embrace the occasion and deliberately put a positive spin on it. When we can recognize and appreciate potentially funny situations, it helps us build emotional resiliency. We laugh and move on . . . at least until the *next* time the oral surgeon comes to town!

"Nothing is quite as funny
as the unintended humor of reality."

~ Steve Allen

Chapter 5
It Takes a Village: Humor and Your OR Team

As an Operating Room nurse, you know that your OR team can be a great source of encouragement and support. The high-pressure, intense environment we function in, coupled with the demanding work we do, can bring out the best in all of us.

Of course, as an OR nurse, you also know that that same OR team can be the reason you *need* so much encouragement and support! As a Swiss health-economist said:

"Nursing would be a dream job— if there were no doctors!"

~ Gerhard Kocker

Over the course of researching this book, I've heard more than a few stories about surgeons losing their cool in the OR. Verbal tirades, scathing sarcasm, even scalpels flung across the room—we'd all like to say that this type of behavior isn't tolerated anymore—but the sad truth is that those moments do happen. As professionals we need the skills to deal with this kind of outburst, and move past them. After all, there's always another patient waiting in pre-op.

Humor helps. In fact, humor is probably the best coping mechanism to use when you must consistently deliver top performance in a high-stress environment. This is when we see humor functioning as a social lubricant. Laughter makes it easier to start and maintain healthy relationships. In this section, we'll be discussing ten ways OR nurses use humor to support (and survive!) their colleagues.

(1) Create a Safe Space to Process Emotions Thru Humor

> "Most of the surgeons we work with here are great, but there's one who… well, let's say she's got a short temper. She likes everything *just so*, and if something's not right, you're going to hear about it!
>
> "And here's the thing. She looks like Paula Deen. I mean spitting image

> here—the two of them could be twins. So every time Doc gets on one of her tirades, I just sit back and say to myself, 'Y'all go on with your bad self now, Paula!' and picture her serving up ooey-gooey butter cake to everyone she's shouting at. It helps me keep my cool . . ."

This OR nurse, who wishes to remain anonymous—[and if you happen to know a surgeon who looks just like Paula Deen, don't you DARE spill the beans!]—is demonstrating the use of humor to distance oneself from an emotionally charged situation.

It's not pleasant to be on the receiving end of someone else's bad day. And let's be real—after the first five seconds or so of hearing about what wasn't done right, you've got the message to do it differently next time. Every bit of lecture after that is just extraneous information, generally heavy on the emotion and short on the value. Shifting your attention (at least internally) to a subject you find amusing is a good way to create a buffer between yourself and the anger or frustration being vented at you.

I call this "Humor Visualization." No one has to know the picture going on inside your head! This humor is just for you. This is a variation of an old humor technique used to help people who are nervous about public speaking to overcome their fear. All you have to do is picture everyone in the audience in their underwear!

When we're feeling under attack, it's very hard to perform at our best. Viewing the person or people who are provoking undesirable emotions or stress within you through a humorous framework levels the power imbalance, making it easier to function at the highest level.

Humor shared is humor increased.

> ". . . Of course, I'm not the only person who's noticed that this doc looks like Paula Deen. Sometimes, she's going on-and-on, and I glance at the circulating nurse, and I know she's thinking the exact same thing I am. It makes it hard not to laugh!"

Sharing humor can create a valuable sense of solidarity, strengthening the bonds among team members.

(2) Build a Humor Library: For OR Staff Only!

One quick and simple way to support the humor habit among your OR team is to build a humor library. Don't worry—there are no building permits required! A humor library can be as simple as a binder filled with cartoons, funny stories, and jokes that make you laugh out loud.

Leave it in the staff lounge or break room where anyone can enjoy and add to it—with the understanding that while all material is intended for the OR team, it could, at any time, be read by *anyone* in the building. It's a good idea to keep things family-friendly and positive for that reason.

Your humor library could include books, magazines and funny movies on DVD, as well as cartoons, newspaper clippings and jokes. Online resources, such as invitation-only Facebook groups, are a great way to share jokes and humor with your team.

Don't be afraid to think outside the box!

(3) Level the Playing Field with Humor

Every member of the OR team has a critical and vital role to play, with specific contributions to make to the patient's successful outcome. Every member of the OR team is a highly trained healthcare professional. However, every member of the OR team doesn't receive the same amount of social recognition or validation for their professional skills—from the general public, or even from each other.

For a number of cultural and social reasons, a hierarchy has emerged over time with surgeons receiving the lion's share of prestige and respect. This hierarchal dynamic pervades the OR suite, with each person finding a role to occupy based on position, experience, and gender.

Like all hierarchies, things look pretty good from the top. But if you're lower down on the totem pole, things aren't so great. Leveling social hierarchies as much as possible enhances team functionality, particularly when that team needs to function in a high-stress environment.

Humor levels social hierarchies. When people laugh together over shared experiences, for that moment, they're all on the same level. There is no upper-or-lower, better-or-worse. The surgeon is on the same footing as the scrub nurse. Humor illustrates what we have in common, rather than focusing on those factors that differentiate us from each other.

> "Our surgeon and our scrub nurse were both avid gardeners. One day they'd spent quite a bit of time talking about all the plants they'd put in, including that beautiful vining plant, the clematis.
>
> "The next time they worked together, the scrub nurse, remembering the previous conversation, cheerfully inquired of the surgeon, 'So, how's your chlamydia doing?'
>
> "After the nurse removed her foot from her mouth, she and the surgeon

shared a gut-busting laugh that went on for several minutes!"

(4) Support Others with Humor

"At times, patients to come to us from the local correctional facility. They come in with shackles and handcuffs and a guard. Some of these guys are really large and pretty intimidating, but generally they're not a problem. Still, we're all keenly aware when there are prisoners on the unit.

"So . . . We have this one guy on the table, and everything's fine—except for the guard who's required to be in the room to observe. The circulating nurse notices that he was getting a little green and wobbly. Before he could faint dead away, she told him, quite sternly and loudly, *"Get down on the floor!"*

"Meanwhile . . . in the adjoining suite . . . a nurse heard the command, thought the prisoner was trying to escape—*so she hit the floor!"*

[Really, folks, you don't have to make this stuff up!]

There was lots of laughter in both OR suites after the situation was clarified. These moments are funny—but they can also speak volumes about the many stresses and pressures that come with OR nursing. Our training and professional ethics tell us to treat all patients equally—which is lovely in theory but can be pretty difficult when you've got a patient who's doing 25-to-life for tearing up a SWAT team with his bare hands. This creates an internal tension, which we usually suppress. Then a crisis happens—or as in the case of this incident, is perceived to be happening—and we react from a very visceral, emotional place.

Laugher is good exercise. Really.

Laughter is a universal lauguage—across cultures and across ages.

Laughter is just plain fun!

Put yourself in that nurse's shoes. What feelings was she experiencing when she hit the floor? There was undoubtedly a great deal of fear, anxiety, and terror. There she was, as far as she knew, in a scene from Rambo! Our bodies don't react to what's *actually* happening—they react to what we *perceive* is happening. This means her system was flooded with adrenaline. That fight-or-flight response was fully engaged.

Discovering that the problem was a woozy guard,

and not an escape attempt resolves the issue—but this knowledge doesn't immediately alleviate the physiological and psychological responses to stress. That's where laughter comes in. It is an almost universal reaction to use humor to address this type of emotional roller coaster situation. Laughter can restore a sense of emotional stability. It is our way of acknowledging that everything is okay after all, while owning the fact we had a significant emotional reaction to events.

Humor among colleagues can be a great way to build strong bonds between team members (and you'd better believe there were lots of prison-break jokes in *that* OR in the days and weeks that followed!). Whether they were consciously aware of it or not, everyone knew that it could very easily have been *them* in the same situation. The ability of the group to see the funny side of what could have been a bad situation strengthened the team's collective humor habit. This will make it easier for them to draw on humor, and cope effectively when another challenging situation arises.

. . . And at a different hospital that treats inmates:

> "By and large, the inmates go out of their way to be polite and respectful while they're here. Sometimes, they're actually pretty funny people.

> "During the standard pre-op questioning, one of our nurses asked an inmate about his understanding of the procedure he was about to undergo. Her exact words were 'What are you in for?'
>
> "Without hesitation the inmate smiled and replied, 'Grand Theft Auto.' "

Of course, it's important that we, as OR nurses, are always mindful of the dignity of our patients. It is always better to laugh *with* someone than laugh *at* them. As profound as our need for stress relief may be, our patients often need that stress relief even more than we do . . .

> "About five years ago, I was interviewing one of my patients preoperatively. This gentle man, and I do mean gentle-man, was about to have a revision to his AV fistula that was being used for dialysis. He was also a convict from a local prison, and—because he was potentially violent—was handcuffed, and accompanied by a large, intimidating guard who was standing nearby.

"While I was interviewing this 40-something African American patient, I covered him with a warm blanket. When he asked me to say a prayer with him, I held his hand. After saying 'Amen' together, he started crying. He thanked me profusely for my kindness because it wasn't how he had expected to be treated.

"He was alone and scared, just like my other patients, but he was touched by my compassion. It's one of the core values of nursing, and it really does apply to every single patient.

"This gentle man went on to explain that he had done 'bad things' in his life, and that people usually feared or disrespected him. Regardless, he was my patient, and deserved my undivided attention and care.

"I believe that acting in this manner is more than just a nurse's mission, it is an essential part of our calling. Some people don't believe that OR nursing is 'real' nursing because we, for the most part, interact less with our

> patients than most nurses do. We whisk them off to the OR where they are soon put under general anesthesia or sedation.
>
> "But, I think it is more accurate to say that OR nurses must possess superior skills at establishing trust and rapport with our patients very quickly. We usually have less than five minutes to assess the patient, acquaint him with the procedure, and then take him away from his loved ones, and into the OR for the ride of his life."

(5) Boost Morale with Humor

Humor can play a vital role in setting the emotional tone in any organization or community. Laughter improves our mood. This is important to know, because in an environment as complex and dynamic as an OR, there are going to be times when the situation looks really bleak.

> "Our OR team is excellent. Really excellent, with awesome surgeons and a team of nurses that are the best I've ever worked with. We do great work. You can never guarantee a good out-

come, of course, but we were in a position where it had been a long time since anything had gone wrong.

"And then we had The Week From Hell. I don't know what it was, but every single day that week, something bad happened. We had a patient code—and that didn't end well. The very next day, our surgeon nicked an artery during a procedure—and there were major complications. We lost another patient the next day—a little old lady who could have been my Grandma. It just kept going like that, day-after-day. We were all walking around in a state of shock. This just wasn't how we did things.

"Then our OR manager found some Far Side comics that were wonderfully dark and twisted. She taped dozens of them all over the OR locker room. Never said a word about them—just stuck them up and walked away.And every day for a week she'd slap up a new one. They-were-funny! (In a warped, OR nurse kind-of-way!)

> "Hearing everyone laughing at them—it doesn't seem like it should be such a big deal—but it really made a difference. Our staff started to emerge from the zombie-like state we'd been in. We started to feel like ourselves again."

In the OR, we go through some pretty intense experiences. Routine procedures suddenly aren't routine at all. Trauma cases are inherently more stressful. The patients we're pulling for the most, sometimes don't do very well. There are problems even the most skilled surgeon can't fix. Every team will experience sad times, grieving times and healing times. Humor can play a role in easing the transition from grieving to healing. Laughing after loss is important in a team's journey back to equilibrium.

The key to using humor in these instances is to be subtle and strategic. A little laughter can go a long way. Visual humor, such as cartoons or funny pictures, delivers a lot of bang for the buck. That's because we process imagery differently than we do text or spoken words. The laughter comes faster, and more automatically—bypassing the self-imposed filters we often place on ourselves when we feel sad or depressed. The mood-lifting benefits of laughter are near immediate; even a *little* laughter will have some positive effect on team morale.

(6) Recognize & Reward Using Humor

When was the last time someone told you that you did a good job? When was the last time *you* expressed your admiration to a colleague for the fine work they do?

It's important to make the time. There are benefits to recognition and appreciation that go beyond just feeling good. These benefits begin with team building. Organizations that have a culture of recognition, especially peer-to-peer recognition, have strong bonds among team members, with fewer problems of absenteeism, stronger morale, and better performance than organizations that don't have the same focus on recognition. When we feel like we're playing a vital and valued role we're more invested in our performance: We work harder, and we're likely to stick around longer.

Recognition has some serious benefits, but that doesn't mean you can't have fun with the process. In fact, light-hearted and humorous forms of appreciation are often the most well received, and are the easiest to incorporate into even the busiest of environments. Appreciation works best when it's personally relevant.

One great example is the surgeon who recognized the team's circulating nurse with the "Golden Abacus Award"—because she did such a great job making sure the number of sponges and clamps that were *removed* from patients equaled the number of sponges and clamps that went *into* the patients in the first place. While this award was never officially recognized or acknowledged by the hospital, the nurse in question kept it taped onto the front of her locker for months.

> ***"The ability to laugh—either naturally or as a learned behavior—may have important implications in societies such as the U.S. where heart disease remains the number one killer."***
>
> ***~ Dr. Michael Miller***

Look for opportunities to create your own organization-specific recognition traditions. One Outpatient Surgery team in Florida has a bright pink plastic lawn flamingo—dressed in surgical scrubs, of course—that is passed from team member to team member monthly, as each person is recognized for what he or she does. Posing with the flamingo and having their picture posted prominently in the practice is part of the tradition.

(7) Create Shared History with Humor

> "Otis elevator," said the surgeon. Nothing. The surgeon raised his eyebrow at the fledgling circulating nurse. *"We need an Otis elevator in here!"*
>
> Bob, the circulating nurse, peered frantically at the instrument tray. Nothing. Panicked—but trying desperately not to show it—he headed out of the OR suite to locate the elusive 'Otis' elevator. He'd almost made it out the door before a kind-hearted nurse stopped him and explained, "It's a joke. He's teasing you! 'Otis' is the name of the company that makes the elevators that you ride up and down in—get it?"

This type of gentle teasing often serves as a rite of passage for new members of an OR team. The close bonds and tight relationships so characteristic of an OR team don't happen overnight. They take nurturing and cultivation. Sending a new team member to the lab for a "blue fallopian tube"—where the lab, understanding what's going on, will invariably reply that they only have *red* fallopian tubes—is a welcoming process.

The use of humor is one way groups signal to new members that they are accepted; that they belong.

Humor builds history among individuals. Bob, the circulating nurse, will never forget the surgeon who sent him searching for an Otis elevator. It's a story he will share with many others—each of whom probably have their *own* rite-of-passage tale to tell. It's important, as a team, that this experience be friendly and welcoming, rather than mean-spirited and hostile. Tone is important. After the fact, this type of humor will be a source of delight for all of the team members. It's a matter of laughing *with*, rather than laughing *at*.

(8) Fight Frustration with Fun

True story . . .

> Ginny, the OR supervisor, picked-up the phone.
>
> "What do you *mean*, you don't know where the patient is?" It was remarkable how calm she was, especially since the surgeon hovering over her shoulder was growing more impatient by the minute. The man was practically shaking with anger.

Still on the phone, Ginny listened, nodded, and said, "Let me know when you find him," and hung up.

"They lost him," she announced matter-of-factly to the assembled surgical team. "Right now, nobody knows where he is."

Silence greeted her announcement. In this sprawling hospital, there were four different buildings where ambulatory care was provided. The patient may have been taken to *any* of them. Such things had happened before.

But in *this* case? The gastric bypass patient in question weighed 650 pounds.

"How, exactly . . ." the surgeon muttered, ". . . did they lose somebody that size?"

The circulating nurse shrugged. "They must practice!"

"Yes," the OR supervisor agreed. "They start with peds patients and then work their way up until they can lose the really big ones!"

If there's one personality trait we can identify as being common among the vast majority of OR nurses, it's the fact that we like to be in control. Our entire profession has developed complex systems to ensure that every possible circumstance that could arise during surgery has been dealt with in advance. We're like the Boy Scouts—"Be prepared!"

Humor creates community.

Humor builds history.

Humor helps people accept change.

But there *are* situations that crop up, every now and then, that you simply can't prepare for. Sometimes the patients get lost on their way to pre-op. Sometimes the surgeon gets lost on his way to the hospital! Things happen, and you can't do anything about them. There's no amount of preparation that would prevent them. And this results in frustration and anger.

Laughter is the best way to dispel this frustration and anger. There's no point in getting angrier about the situation. The patient won't be found any faster—no matter how high your blood pressure gets. In this instance, we see humor used to acknowledge the ridiculousness of the situation, dispel the associated frustration, and encourage the group to move on.

(9) Keep Your Head When the S*** Hits the Fan

Through the course of your career as an OR nurse, things will happen which nothing—and I mean absolutely *nothing!*—you learned in nursing school has prepared you for . . .

> [Another honest-to-goodness Real Life story from the files of Karyn Buxman, RN.]
>
> To this day, I remember the shocked, stunned silence that filled the operating suite when the surgeon dropped the vein he'd just spent a whole hour harvesting from the patient's leg to use for a graft. The vein flipped out of his hand, did a 360 in the air, and then flopped onto the floor.
>
> At a moment like this, *nothing* is funny. It's such a surreal moment. Had everyone not been wearing a mask, you would have seen a roomful of mouths gaping open! You're not even sure what you've just seen happen is real.
>
> Once the vein had been retrieved, rinsed thoroughly and 'blessed' with Betadine, and the procedure was

> completed successfully, the surgeon and the rest of the OR team needed to deal with the emotions that accompanied such an unexpected turn of events.
>
> Once the shock wore off, we laughed at the sheer absurdity of the situation. In such a technologically and medically advanced setting, who would have thought that a simple case of butterfingers could cause so much drama?
>
> And we laughed and laughed in sheer relief that everything turned out okay after all.
>
> [If you haven't experienced this particular phenomenon for yourself, check out Season 1, Episode 1.9 of *Chicago Hope*, titled "Heartbreak."]

If you find yourself or your colleagues laughing in the aftermath of such an event, try to remember that this is a healthy way to process complex emotions. Some people may be able to laugh *immediately* after something bad happens in the OR. For other people, it may take a little time . . .

> "We were doing a breast augmentation, putting in implants post radical

mastectomy. Back in the day, this type of breast implant did not come pre-sterilized. So we had to autoclave them prior to implantation. One vital step was to open a vent port so that the implant wouldn't blow-up from the temperature in the autoclave. This time, the nurse forgot this one vital step. [Now, don't get ahead of our story here!]

"When she brought the first implant into the room, she was in the most incredible state! She was half-crying and half-laughing, with a few expletives thrown in for good measure. The implant, originally the size of an orange, had blown-up to the size of a watermelon! The implant was obviously ruined. And as Murphy's Law would predict, it was the *only* implant of the needed size.

"So, unfortunately, we simply could not complete the procedure at that time.

"Needless to say, the doctor wasn't happy—but that's life in the OR. It took months before we could see the humor in the situation.

> "Since those days, we've come a long way, and there are very specific protocols to follow, and implants are now pre-sterilized. But some of us can look back fondly on those unexpected learning experiences and chuckle."

And so, when the s*** hits the fan—or when the procedure goes haywire—the OR nurse's first line of defense is quick thinking. And your second line of defense is gaining perspective somehow. And this is where your sense of humor can be invaluable.

(10) Upping *Others'* Attitudes—By Upping *Yours*

Ken Keyes has a powerful and thought-provoking quote. "A loving person lives in a loving world. A hostile person lives in a hostile world. Everyone you meet is your mirror." The experiences we have are directly and significantly impacted by the attitude we, ourselves, have. Or, as the Bible puts it, "Seek, and ye shall find." (Matthew 7:7)

What does this mean? Obviously, we don't have the ability to control how other people conduct themselves when they're around us. It would be nice if we did: Imagine never losing a parking space again! Life would be so much easier if people would act the way we wanted them to.

But while we can't *control* other people, we *do* have

the ability to *influence* how they act. The way we do that is, as Keyes suggests, with our own behavior. It's an easy theory to test:

On day one, *smile* at everyone you see. Take note of how many people smile back, or are cheerful and happy in your presence.

Humor helps some people reduce their bad cholesterol (LDL) while increasing their good cholesterol (HDL).

And then, on day two, *frown* at everyone you see. Again, take note of how people react. You'll hear a lot more complaining and negativity when you greet the world with a negative expression. There's a lot of fascinating research being conducted regarding the complex social and physiological reasons why this phenomenon happens, but there's no arguing that it does happen.

Chances are that your day as an OR nurse would be far more pleasant and satisfying if you were surrounded by people who were, by and large, in a good mood and happy to see you. You can stack the deck in favor of this happening by being in a good mood yourself. Humor plays a huge role in this. Learning to see and appreciate the funny moments in life makes it easier to keep smiling. Sharing humor makes other people happier as well. And happier people are nicer to be around, and ergo, your day gets better.

[Ta-daa!]

"Humor is a rubber sword—
it allows you to make a point
without drawing blood."

~ Mary Hirsch

Chapter 6

So . . . What IS so Funny About Humor and the OR Nurse?

We've talked about the *patient.* We've talked about the *team* you work with. Now it's time to talk about *you*, the OR nurse.

Our profession has many rewards. It also has many challenges. In order to thrive, personally and professionally, it's essential—we absolutely *must*—take an active role in our own self-care. We can't count on others to provide the support and validation we need.

Let me level with you here: Self-care isn't always easy. Living a healthy and balanced life is an admirable goal—but it's not a goal that's necessarily compatible with the demands of OR nursing. We all know a healthy diet is important—

and yet most surgical break rooms are filled with goodies from the four basic food groups: Caffeine, sugar, salt, and fat. One soon discovers that scrubs can effectively cover a multitude of sins—and pounds!

A Tweet regarding OR staff: "They're like seagulls. They'll eat anything."

Some nurses are fans of exercise as a stress-buster. I think every team has one of these folks—you know the type who goes for a twelve-mile run *after* a twelve-hour shift. The rest of us mere mortals work up a sweat just thinking about such a thing.

> ***"A merry heart doeth good like a medicine."***
>
> ***Proverbs 17:22***

This is where humor comes in. Laughter is 100% portable, always available, and best of all, it's free. Cultivating the humor habit—learning to see the funny that surrounds us every day—makes every day as an OR nurse just a little bit easier. Laughter lifts the spirits, restores emotional resiliency, and lowers stress levels.

To be a happier, healthier, more effective OR nurse, laugh every day.

Easier said than done, you say? Not true, say I! Here are many ways for you to make "finding the funny" a part of your daily routine. These techniques are simple, fast, cheap and fun.

Think of this as the Grand Buffet of Humor. Take what you like and leave the rest! Don't feel obligated to pile everything onto your plate. [Good news: Unlike smorgasbords, excessive humor does not lead to "muffin tops."]

Humor is deeply personal. As you read through these pages, you'll find that some techniques and strategies make you laugh out loud, while others won't seem so funny. You'll realize maximum benefits by choosing and practicing those techniques and strategies that resonate with you.

Choose from among the following eight humor strategies the ones that make *you* laugh, that *you* enjoy, and that feel more like play than work—to *you!* [That's how it's supposed to work!]

(1) Be a Humor Collector

The goal here is to laugh every day. The challenge is to figure out exactly *how* to make this happen. One thing I've found, over the course of more than two decades of focused research, is that the world is a really, really funny place. The trick is to keep your eyes open, pay attention, and be aware of the humorous things that are happening all around you.

In the olden days, I used to recommend people create a library of humorous books, cartoons, and records from their favorite comedians.

Today, things are so much easier. You can build a fabulous humor collection on your computer or smart phone, if you're so inclined. There are joke-of-the-day websites, funny blogs, and as many humorous books as you can load onto your Kindle. Create your own YouTube channel of funny videos; set up your Netflix queue with the best comedies ever.

Give yourself the freedom to create a humor collection that is wholly and completely your own. It's all about *you!* What makes *you* laugh? Remember, this is your own private source of amusement—if you're tickled beyond all reason by pictures of basset hounds wearing Easter bonnets, no one needs to know. [Your secret is safe with me!]

Finding items to put in your humor collection is only half the fun. The other half is experiencing these funny items again and again. Whenever you're feeling down, or in need of a smile, check out your humor collection. Something in there is sure to make you laugh. It's a fast way to lift your spirits.

Here's a piece to get you started:

THE TOP 10 "YOU KNOW YOU'RE AN OR NURSE WHEN . . ."

10. *Nothing surprises you.*

9. *You can only tell time with a 24-hour clock.*

8. *The surgeons still won't respect you in the morning, even after you've spent all night with them.*

7. *Your nursing shoes have been seized and held in quarantine by the CDC, OSHA, or the Department of Homeland Security.*

6. *Your family won't let you discuss your day at work at the dinner table . . . EVER.*

5. *There are three kinds of soap in your bathroom—and a scrub brush!*

4. *All of your shoes are comfortable.*

3. *Hemostats are a handy household tool!*

2. *You bring lunch leftovers home in a bio-hazard bag—without a second thought.*

1. *You no longer have a gag reflex.*

(2) Raise Your Awareness

Every day contains humor. Some days this humor is more apparent than others. Sometimes laughter is easy to find. Sometimes, you have to look for it. I refer to the strategy of actively seeking out humor as "Raising Awareness." Raising Awareness means choosing to recognize the funny side of life and deliberately cultivating laughter and mirth.

Raising Awareness also means choosing to ask questions like, "What's So Funny About OR Nursing?" So many OR nurses I spoke with in the course of researching this book initially responded to that question in the same way: "Nothing! There's *nothing* funny about OR nursing!" That response was delivered in a variety of tones. Sometimes the nurses were resentful and sad; other times, they were angry and frustrated. But as the conversations went on, and we delved into the individual experiences of each OR nurse, a trend emerged. Each and every one of them had funny stories to share. The process of simply stopping and searching through their professional memories brought to mind the silly

> ***Humor fights frustration.***
>
> ***Humor helps people support others.***
>
> ***Humor provides perspective.***

and the sublime, the sarcastic and the side-splittingly hysterical.

Recognizing those moments is the first step in answering: "What is there to laugh about?" When you can do that, you will then have a skill that you can carry with you anywhere, and use any time. Using this skill will improve the quality of your work and your life.

It's a lot easier to *see* funny than to *be* funny, and it's more valuable, too. Seeing funny is one of the easiest ways to integrate humor into your life. In fact, once you start, you might not be able to stop!

"If I hadn't believed it, I wouldn't have seen it."

~ Ashleigh Brilliant

The first step in seeing funny is to assume that there is funny to be seen. If your worldview tells you that there's nothing funny happening in your life, then you'll be right. On the other hand, if you believe that the world is an amusing place just waiting for you to discover it, then you'll be right, too.

> "It's not unusual for many of our patients to mispronounce the procedure they're having, or even the condition they have. Instead of having a

> colonoscopy, they're coming in for their 'colostomy.' Instead of varicose veins, they need surgery on their 'very close veins.' Instead of fixing their rotator cuff, they're here to get their 'rotary cuff' fixed . . . that sort of thing. But my absolute favorite is the little old lady who told me, with total sincerity, as we were walking her out from her breast biopsy, 'Honey, that's the best 'autopsy' I've ever had!' "

And sometimes Raising Awareness merely means being open to recognizing humor when it presents itself . . .

> "Several pediatric patients had been sent to the OR with their pre-op injection sites much higher than the gluteus maximus. This posed a risk to the youngsters, and our anesthesiologist was determined to get to the bottom of the problem.
>
> "So he marched over to where our next patient was waiting. He glared down at the six-year-old boy and asked him, "Where did you get your shot?"

> "The little guy, eyes wide at the sight of the looming masked figure, meekly replied, 'In my room.'
>
> "The anesthesiologist paused, leaned his head against the wall, and was grateful that his mask hid his uncontrollable laughter."

Let yourself believe that the world is full of humor. Just taking this simple step will place you light years ahead of those around you who are in too much of a hurry to take a moment to see and hear and experience the vast absurdity and delight going on all around us.

"From there to here,

and here to there,

funny things are everywhere."

~ Dr. Seuss

How often have you heard something hysterical in the OR, but just couldn't remember it the next day? Well, one person who takes the time to record funny comments in the OR is @ORDailyQuote (a prolific tweeter). He's not necessarily a *creator* of humor, but rather an observer and collector of humor. ("I don't tell 'em what to say. I just quote 'em.") Further, he loves to share his humorous observations with the world. Now, a lot of laymen won't get—or appreciate—these observations, because there's a lot of inside humor here. But what the heck, it's all about *us*, isn't it?!

To wit:

> *Everyone say a prayer to the gods of homeostasis.*
>
> *ENT surgeon while making his incision: "A scar is born."*
>
> *Presurgical RN, in reference to a patient who can't hold still: "He's like a weasel on a stick."*
>
> *Urologist: "It all comes down to the jerk at the end of the suture."*
>
> *First assistant: "I'm the ureter whisperer."*
>
> *Tech palpating a clotted AV fistula: "The thrill is gone."*
>
> *"I have angered the call gods, and I don't know how to appease them."*
>
> *Anesthesiologist, while performing a fiberoptic intubation and looking into the scope: "I think I see the Chilean miners!"*
>
> *Spine surgeon to x-ray tech: "Give us some radar love."*

RN: "He's throwing things at me." Scrub tech: "No, he's got better aim than that."

Anesthesiologist: "Hope is not a plan."

Scrub tech: "My pee smells like coffee."

Circulating Nurse, regarding Scrub Nurse: "We call her by her Indian name, Running Commentary."

You, too, can follow our fellow recorder-of-OR-humor on Twitter at www.Twitter.com/ORDailyQuote.

(3) Look for the Humor Around You: *Visual* Humor

Cartoons, comics and other funny pictures can provide almost instant laughs, and are yours for the clipping. But don't stop there! To get more mileage out of the cartoons, *personalize* them! Write-in people's names or places of interest (surgeons, nurses, administrators—anyone's fair game, but it's a good idea to stick to people who have a good sense of humor). Tape the cartoons on the locker room door.

Massage your creativity! White-Out the captions and let everyone come up with their own.

And to further stretch your brain: *The New Yorker* magazine is well known for its cartoon caption contest, wherein the editors present readers with a cartoon without a caption. The challenge is to write your own caption, then submit it for possible publication. From thousands of submissions weekly, the editors choose their three favorites, then print them in the magazine; the public then votes for their favorites, and the winner becomes world-famous by having his or her caption featured in *The New Yorker!* (This could be something you do on your own—or something you brainstorm with your OR team.) [Don't get the magazine? You can participate online. Visit www.NewYorker.com/humor/caption.]

Recent studies show that people who actively use humor have lower levels of markers for inflammation (C-reactive proteins and cytokines) which lead to atherosclerosis and cardiovascular disease.

Some great sources for *nursing* cartoons include JournalOfNursingJocularity.com (featuring the infamous "Nurse Marge in Charge"); Nurstoon.com (tons of nursing topics) by funnyman Carl Elbing; and ScrubsMagazine.com (featuring a variety of different cartoonists). You can also view tons of syndicated cartoons (Peanuts, Cathy, Blondie, Garfield, Ziggy, etc.) at GoComics.com. Or, if you just like dark humor in general, check out CallahanOnline.com!

(4) Listen for the Humor Around You: *Verbal* Humor

Sharing verbal humor can be done in two ways. The first is telling jokes. The second is by sharing funny stories.

Jokes

If you hear a great joke, pass it on! Humor shared is humor increased.

Q: What's the difference between a surgeon and a puppy?

A: Eventually the puppy grows up and quits whining.

A word to the wise: When you don't know your audience well, stay away from political jokes, religious jokes, alcohol-related stories, racial observations, gender put-downs, yo-mama jokes, jokes in "bad taste" (although this is often hard to judge), and what most people would consider "sick humor." [But see my special section on sick humor. It's enlightening.]

Here are some stories and jokes that have been OR-tested and nurse-approved . . .

During a urological procedure in the OR, the surgeon asked for Van Buren sounds, which are urethral dilators. The circulating nurse promptly went to the

CD player, browsed through the discs, and said, "I can't locate the Van Buren sounds. Are they a new group?"

A surgeon, a lawyer and a businessman were floating in the ocean after their boat sank. Soon they were surrounded by ravenous sharks. The sharks quickly ate the surgeon and the businessman, but left the lawyer alone.

Later, when rescued, the lawyer was asked by the media how he had survived.

The lawyer just shrugged and said, "Professional courtesy."

A patient was admitted for GI bleeding. During the workup, the intern said, "The nurse told me you had some coffee ground emesis."

"Oh, I don't think so," replied the patient. "I only drink tea."

Did you ever notice how you get an itch only after you're fully scrubbed up, gowned and gloved?

The scene: A post-op bed near you. The nurse, brisk, efficient, and cheerful, is checking over her most recent admit, who seems to be through the worst of it.

"How are you feeling?" she asks.

"Great! I just wish the surgeon hadn't used that four-letter word during my procedure."

"Four letter word?!" The nurse is shocked. She knows this surgeon—a professional and sensitive woman. "What in the world did she say?"

"OOPS!"

Four doctors were out duck hunting on a lake. But it was open season for only one species of duck.

After many hours on the boat without seeing a single duck, they all dozed off.

The general practitioner awoke to see a whole flock of ducks flying overhead.

Unsure if they were the ducks currently in season, he roused and consulted with the specialist.

The specialist wasn't sure, so he woke up the surgeon. As soon as the surgeon saw the ducks, he started blasting away.

"Are you sure those ducks are in season?" the first two doctors asked.

The surgeon replied, "Wake the pathologist and ask *him!*"

A patient came into the recovery room after an appendectomy. Everything looked fine, but he kept complaining about a terrible headache and tenderness on the side of his head.

There was no reason why he should be having pain there. The doctor was called, just to check that this wasn't some unusual complication.

"Don't worry about it!" he replied. "I'm not surprised he has a headache. We ran out of anesthesia halfway through the procedure."

Stories

Funny stories, drawn from our own experiences, can play a great role in creating strong bonds your OR team. More than that, they're fun to tell. Your colleagues will laugh, and you get to laugh along with them, experiencing all of the mental and physical benefits of humor.

If you want to *really* connect with people, you may want to develop your skills at story-telling. As they say, practice makes perfect. (Note: It is easier to tell a good *story* than it is to tell a good *joke*.)

Become a collector of stories. Seek them from the people you work with every day. Ask what their favorite funny memory is, what makes them laugh, what's their most embarrassing moment.

You'll get two benefits from doing this. First, others will see you as a humorous person. And second, you'll now have a repertoire of stories that you can share with others.

There are some stories that are universal to operating rooms everywhere. Every team—every surgeon, nurse and tech, in fact—will have their own versions of these stories. One classic tale is the "You have WHAT lodged WHERE??" story. [I'm not judging—just observing.] In fact, there's an entire book devoted to this topic: *Stuck Up! 100 Objects Inserted and Ingested Where They Shouldn't Be.* [You just don't have to make this stuff up . . .]

One OR nurse I interviewed for this book had her own story of "You Have WHAT lodged WHERE??"

> "I remember the first time we got this kind of call from the ER . . . They had a guy with a vibrator lodged in his rectum. I kept waiting for the punch line, but no, that was the whole story.
>
> "It's worth noting that we're a small town and nothing like this had ever happened at our hospital before. Anyway, they send the patient up to the OR. Our doc was a curmudgeonly sixty-something gentleman, and rather conservative . . . So as you can

> imagine, he was rather uncomfortable with the situation.
>
> "We got the patient to sleep, and positioned his feet in the stirrups. The doctor was just about to do what needed to be done, when the anesthesiologist stopped him and said, 'Remember, this thing doesn't *need* to come out—he's just in here for a battery change!' "

In this instance, the use of humor successfully dispursed some of the tension the doctor was experiencing. And this had a positive impact on the outcome. Our emotions don't stop when we walk into the OR. The use of humor can help us process those emotions in an efficient, appropriate way.

And—as if one such story wasn't enough . . .

> In a small, rural hospital in Canada, a young man came into the hospital with a soda bottle lodged in his rectum. The patient explained that he had "slipped in the shower" and fell onto the bottle. The bottle was removed and the patient was discharged.

A week later, the same fellow returned, once again with a soda bottle lodged in his rectum. Again, he explained that he had "slipped in the shower," falling onto the soda bottle. The bottle was removed and the patient was discharged.

Several weeks later, the fellow returned to the hospital once again, and—you guessed it—had a soda bottle lodged in his rectum from a "fall in the shower."

This time, when the patient was discharged, the long-time physician wrote in his discharges orders, "Son, if I were you, I'd stop drinking soda in the shower."

(5) Play Around!

Playful people are happier people. Happy people are healthier people. This is true for everyone, but it's especially true for OR nurses. One of the best ways to introduce humor into your day, and become a happier, stronger, calmer caregiver is to embrace the power of play.

Playing, having fun, using your imagination . . . once upon a time, these were our only jobs in the world. When we were kids, life was all about playing. Then, as adult responsibilities began piling up, less and less time became available for playing. We've gotten too busy to have fun.

"We do not stop playing because we grow old; we grow old beause we have stopped playing."

~ BENJAMIN FRANKLIN

The *time* for play may have disappeared, but the *need* for it has not. We need our imagination, our silliness, our make-believe and clever games, just as much as we did when we were kids. Perhaps even more. Play is incredibly powerful—it lifts the spirit, rejuvenates and energizes, and adds a much-needed element of joy to our days.

Play is incredibly powerful, and yet it is almost universally undervalued. Trust me, I've been paying attention . . . to children, to adults, to patients with many conditions, and to the medical and scientific journals.

Because children play, we consider play to be a

childish thing. Yet nothing could be further from the truth. Play can transform the way we see the world. And let's be real here—after a long day in the OR, sometimes our worldview could do with a little transformation!

Here's one way you can incorporate the power of play into your life: Create a "Play List," full of things that are fun for you to do! It can include playing games, playing sports, playing piano, playing with your kids, playing with your dog (or your kids' dogs, or your dog's kids). At least half your list should be low-cost or no-cost [unless you're both rich *and* an OR nurse, in which case, go wild!].

When you're feeling down, or it's been a really bad day, do at least one thing on your Play List. There is a method to the madness here. When you're most in need of play is when you're least able to think of something fun to do. You're feeling sick or tired or frustrated—nothing sounds like much fun.

So don't wait until you feel better to do the things on your Play List! That would be missing the point. Let play transform your crummy day. Perform an activity from your Play List when you're feeling bad, and I promise, you'll feel better.

"What if the Hokey-Pokey really is what it's all about?"

~ Bumper sticker

Because really, is it possible to have a bad day while doing the Hokey-Pokey??

Bingo!

Put the power of play to work by bringing your whole OR team on board. Even the simplest game can get your team laughing, boosting the group's morale.

One great way to involve the team in play is a little game I created: "What's So Funny About… OR Nursing BINGO!"

Scan the QR code or go to . . .

www.KarynBuxman .com/wpcontent/uploads/ WSFA _ ORNursing_ BingoWhite.pdf

. . . to print copies for your whole team. Play traditional, or four corners, or blackout—your choice. And, of course, there must be prizes of unspeakable value for the winners (things like gummy bears, costume jewelry, marbles, Legos, balloons, bagels, funny buttons, loose change or lottery tickets).

What's so Funny About... O.R. Nursing Bingo

Consent Form Incorrect	Duck! Projectile Vomiting	Behind Schedule!	Working Through Lunch	No Coffee!
NPO Patient Has Eaten	Someone Brought Donuts!	Student Observer	Short Staffed	Staple PT Shut
Doc Stole My Pen	IV Perforates	Free Bingo Space!	Stat X-Ray	A Funny Joke!
Patient Spilled Urinal	Sterile Instrument Dropped	Patient Needs Packed Cells	Anesthesia's Cranky	Love The Music
Surgeon Late for Case	Pre-Op Labs Incomplete	Patient Allergic To More Than 3 Drugs	Foreign Object Where?!	Dr. Thanks Nurse

Scan this code with your smartphone to find a downloadable version of this bingo card and learn other ways to improve global health through humor and laughter.

(6) Laugh for No Reason Whatsoever, a.k.a. Laughter Yoga

What kind of health book would this be if it didn't include at least a passing nod to exercise?! Any time I want to get OR nurses laughing, I recommend a vigorous workout routine of early morning runs, followed by mid-afternoon aerobics, and evening spin classes. This schedule alone is enough to reduce some of you to tears (of laughter).

That's great news, because experts have discovered that even fake laughter has benefits! [No, really!]

Charles Schaefer, a psychology professor at Fairleigh Dickinson University, conducted a study demonstrating that even completely fake laughter can boost mood and overall well-being. In the study, participants were asked to laugh heartily for one full minute. Afterward, they reported feeling better, and having a more positive outlook on life. The study was repeated with similar results, and has inspired the creation of many laughter groups.

Laughter clubs can be found in many locations, particularly if you live near a large city. These can be a great resource, offering a chance to connect with other like-minded individuals. You can learn more by visiting WorldLaughterTour.com to find existing groups or to learn how to form your own laughter club.

Here are some laughter exercises you can try (and these will all work in the privacy of your own home, in case you're uncomfortable looking silly in public).

Flying Bird Laughter

Move around the room, flapping your wings like you are a bird, laughing all the while. Change up the type of bird: Are you a slow moving albatross, gliding over the ocean, or a fast flying hungry eagle zooming to your next meal?

Electric Shock Laughter

Pretend you're getting an electric shock from everything you touch. Give a great big exaggerated response to every pretend shock: Jump up in the air, wave your arms, yell "Ay Carumba!" It won't take long before you're laughing like crazy!

Hula Hoop Laughter

Imagine a Hula Hoop around your hips. Get the hoop moving by swinging your hips in a circular motion, and laugh while you keep the hoop moving.

Hearty Laughter

Laugh while raising both arms toward the sky with your head tilted a little bit backwards. Feel as if the laughter is coming from your heart. Laugh as loud as you can, for as long as you can. It may feel forced at first, but soon you'll find yourself genuinely laughing.

Gradient Laughter

Start by smiling—then slowly begin to laugh with a gentle chuckle. Increase the intensity and volume of the laugh until you've achieved a robust laugh. Then gradually bring the laugh back down to a smile again.

(7) Take the 24-Hour Challenge

Humor shared is humor increased. [It's too bad chocolate doesn't work like that!] If you want to increase the amount of laughter in your life, not to mention the physical and mental benefits associated with humor, I invite you to try the 24-Hour Challenge.

It's really simple. When you find something that makes you laugh out loud, you have 24 hours to share that experience with someone else. Sometimes this is easy. You see a split-your-sides picture on Facebook? Share it with your friends. If it makes you laugh, chances are it will make other people laugh as well.

Hear a great joke? Tell it to the next person you see. See a really funny film? Take your spouse or partner to see it, too. When we laugh with someone, we become closer to that person. Humor creates bonds and connections between us. It's a positive experience that rejuvenates and refreshes.

One of the great side benefits of sharing humor with others is that they're encouraged to share humor with you. When people know that you appreciate a good joke, they'll make a point of telling you good jokes they've heard. You've established yourself as a receptive audience for humor—and you get to reap the rewards in laughter.

Another way to approach the 24-Hour Challenge is to commit to making one person laugh every single day. It's a simple little habit, but one that can have a tremendous impact on your quality of life—and *theirs*!

Let's face it. There are some days when being an OR nurse is not only hard, it's demoralizing. Things—heartbreaking things—can happen, and there's nothing you can do about it. Some things are out of our control. What we *can* control is how we interact with the people around us. When we make someone else smile, it's going to make *us* smile—and that tiny little boost to our spirit and psyche can give us the critical resiliency we need to come back and do the same thing all over again tomorrow.

(8) Decorate for Laughs

Everyone is intensely affected by the environment in which they live. Let's define "living space" as any location where you spend large amounts of time, which includes both home and work. Your living space has a huge impact on the way you view the world and yourself.

The typical OR suite is, by design, cold, clean, and sterile. It's an environment created to facilitate focus and control. There's no place for distraction; no room for anything that might contaminate the sterile field. We're talking about an area low on visual stimuli, with a relatively bland color scheme of chrome, white-or- seafoam-green, and tile.

Laughter lightens one's mood.

Humor supports intimacy.

Frivolity reduces fear.

There's not much that can be done about this. However, it's important to recognize and honor the role our environment has on our psyche. While the integrity of the OR suite must be maintained, there's no law that says you can't decorate areas such as the locker room to elevate the mood. It doesn't take much. Some funny cartoons can be enough to bring a smile to your face. Or, if your team has a "mascot," you might want to keep it where everyone can see it. I've seen lawn flamingos, stuffed polar bears, and even a Tickle-Me-Elmo populating surgical departments around the country.

Another fun idea is to collect pictures of the team

and their pets. Post them separately and see if you can match-up the pairs that belong together. [Some people really *do* look like their dogs. Be prepared. You'll never look at a Chihuahua or Shih Tzu the same way again!]

You can even decorate *yourself*. When circulating, I was known to take a magic marker to decorate my mask with a smile occasionally, or to draw bling on my disposable gloves. My lab coat generally sported buttons with humorous messages, like *"Stop me before I become my mother!"* or *"What's wrong? Is it my hair?"* or *"You have something stuck between your teeth."*

One facility even held a hospital-wide contest: Bedpan Hat Decorations! The hospital provided participants with clean, never-before-used bedpans. The participants provided the creativity, crayons, flowers, streamers, buttons, Slinkeys, tubing, etc.

(9) Let the Music Move You

While you can't do much about making the OR suite *look* more humorous, you *can* make it *sound* funnier! Music is a powerful tool that can lift your mood, elevate your spirits, and positively impact your emotional state. Nurses, anesthetists, and doctors have combined their healthcare expertise with their musical talents to create some unique entertainment. You may want to try introducing some of these tunes by creating a fun OR playlist.

Too Live Nurse (a.k.a., the RNs of Rock) provides stress relief and entertainment with songs and parodies such as "The Girl with Emphysema," "Doin' The Incontinence Rag," and "Ventilate Me." Another ensemble, Dr. Sam and The Managed Care Blues Band, sing about serious healthcare issues with witty tunes like "Capitation Blues," "Managed Healthcare Blues," and "You Picked a Fine Time to Leave Me, Blue Shield." And, of course, there's the Laryngospasms, a group of nurse anesthetists, who combine their sense of humor and musical talents to bring you medical parodies of classic and familiar songs such as "Anesthesia Dreamin'," "Waking Up Is Hard to Do," and "The Little Old Lady with Her Fractured Femur."

(10) Find Someone Who "Gets It"

One of the hazards of being an OR nurse is that you're privy to all kinds of hysterically funny things that happen in the course of a day—and there are very few people in the world who will find those things funny, too. Sure, spouses and partners try, and your friends will indulge you every now and then—but frankly, a lot of what's funny about nursing has to do with blood, boogers, and body fluids. This isn't material that everyone is comfortable thinking about, much less laughing about. Another nurse, however, will know where you're coming from.

> *ENT surgeon during sinus surgery: "That's a lotta boogers."*
>
> *OR nurse's reply: "No it's snot."*

Humor researchers talk about the phenomenon of "insider humor." This is humor that comes from shared experiences. If you haven't had the experience, you might "understand" the joke—but you probably won't find it funny. In fact, you may judge it to be inappropriate, gross or just plain mean.

That's why one OR team I know created a "Dilly Code." This is a private [shhh!] code, the significance of which is known only to OR team personnel. When a Dilly Code is called, all available OR team members converge on a secret location, share a Dilly Bar (a Dairy Queen specialty), and [are you ready?? . . .] just shoot the breeze. (The result? Stress reduction. Stronger bonds. More community. And laughs. Lots and lots of laughs.) Ten minutes spent laughing with your colleagues can have a significant positive impact on everyone's day.

Another way to find professional "soul mates" (those who "get it") is to form friendships with other

OR nurses, locally *and* nationally. Professional association meetings and conventions offer prime opportunities to meet people who have the same sense of humor that you do. Make a point of connecting online, on the phone, or in person, at least every few weeks.

Social media can also provide some great opportunities for sharing your sense of humor when your family thinks you're crazy. One nurse-oriented Facebook source is FB.com/JournalOfNursing Jocularity. And some Twitter sources include @ORDailyQuotes and @FunnyNurse. (Additional resources are listed at the back of this book.)

Five minutes spent laughing with someone who understands can do more than just lift your mood. It's a solid reminder that you're not alone. Other OR nurses are facing the same challenges and obstacles that you are. Working together—and laughing together—makes it easier for all of us.

[This page intentionally left blank.]

"Life should be lived as play."

~ Plato

Chapter 7
The Last Laugh

As a humorist and professional speaker who spends a lot of time traveling, I have to say I *love* Southwest Airlines. These folks use applied humor to keep a group of people who are in a relatively high-stress situation moving, on-task, and generally pleasant. When the flight attendant starts the safety check with the line, "There may be 50 ways to leave your lover, but there's only *four* ways to leave this plane . . ." people laugh—but they also pay attention.

There's another line I heard from a Southwest flight attendant, and it's particularly important information if you happen to be an OR nurse. The flight attendant had reached the part of the safety speech where she was detailing what would happen in the (of course) extremely unlikely event that the plane loses cabin pressure. Oxygen masks would drop down from the ceiling. We could don them, she explained, if continuing to breathe fit into our plans for the afternoon.

That's when she said the magic line. *"If you're traveling with a child, or someone behaving like a child, make sure to put your own oxygen mask on first!"*

Ladies and gentlemen, truer words were never spoken. *Put your own oxygen mask on first.* You have to take care of yourself before you can take care of other people.

Before we go into the OR and do what we do to change our patients' lives for the better, we need to make sure we're looking out for our own physical and emotional health, too. No one is going to do this for us. We need to do it for ourselves.

"Put your own oxygen mask on first."

One great way to do this is to start every day with a laugh—or two. Make humor as important to your morning routine as that first cup of coffee. Before heading out the door, check-out the silly pictures your friends have posted on Facebook. Goof around with your kids before they leave for school. Find a funny drive-time radio show to enjoy. These daily morning laughs are your own personal oxygen mask. Make sure you put it on!

And so . . . To send you on your way with a smile on your face—here's my all-time-favorite OR nurse joke:

> *Three surgeons are walking along a beach. They spot a magic lamp and one of them picks it up and rubs it. Out pops a genie and he says, "I'll grant each of you one wish!"*
>
> *The orthopedic surgeon smiles and says, "Make me 25% smarter then these guys."*
>
> *The genie looks at him, nods, and says, "Your wish is granted! You are now 25% smarter."*
>
> *The cardiac surgeon chuckles and says, "Make me 50% smarter than these guys."*
>
> *The genie looks at him, nods, and says, "Your wish is granted! You are now 50% smarter."*
>
> *The neurosurgeon smirks and says, "Make me 100% smarter than these guys."*
>
> *The genie looks at him, nods, and says, "Your wish is granted! You are now . . . an* OR *nurse!"*

❖ ❖ ❖

4 out of 5 doctors recommend

Online resources can deepen your understanding of applied and therapeutic humor for OR Nurses.

Association for Applied & Therapeutic Humor, www.aath.org
This non-profit organization serves as the community for professionals who study, practice and promote healthy humor. (Non-professionals love it, too.) Includes a monthly ezine, teleconferences, annual conference, CEs, and graduate credit through the Humor Academy.

Callahan Online, www.CallahanOnline.com
The works of cartoonist John Callahan. Contains a lot of dark humor. [Don't let family members sneak a peek!]

Comic-Con, www.Comic-Con.org
An annual gathering of 140,000 fans of popular culture, including movie fans, sci-fi fans, Star Wars aficionados, super hero lovers, and comic book fans.

FunnyNurse, www.Twitter.com/FunnyNurse
Humor for nurses in 140 characters or less. Caution: May contain references to body fluids, death, & dismemberment.

GoComics, www.GoComics.com
Lots and lots (and lots) of your favorite syndicated comic strips. [Peanuts and Cathy and Ziggy, oh my!]

Journal of Nursing Jocularity
www.JournalOfNursingJocularity.com Humor by nurses for nurses. An online salute to the magazine published from 1991-1998 by Doug Fletcher, RN.

www.Facebook.com/JournalOfNursingJocularity
A Facebook group where nurses can share their humorous experiences and observations.

Laughter Yoga
www.LaughterYoga.comhttp://tinyurl.com/8c2jd6t
Founded by Dr. Madan Kataria, Laughter Yoga combines unconditional laughter with yogic breathing (Pranayama). Exercises, events, and information.

The New Yorker Cartoon Caption Contest
www.newyorker.com/humor/caption
A weekly contest where anyone can submit captions to a cartoon provided by The New Yorker. The winners' captions appear in the magazine. No cash prizes, but it's great for bragging rights!

O.R. Quotes, www.Twitter.com/ORDailyQuote
Real quotes from a real operating room.

StoryPeople, www.StoryPeople.com
Unique and playful illustrations, artwork, physical and electronic greeting cards with funny and/or insightful thoughts, by artist/poet Brian Andreas.

What's So Funny About® . . .?
www.WhatsSoFunnyAbout.com
Ongoing information on applied and therapeutic humor for chronic illnesses, including heart disease, diabetes, cancer, Alzheimer's, depression, and more— by Karyn Buxman, RN.

World Laughter Tour
www.WorldLaughterTour.com
Founded by Steve Wilson and Karyn Buxman to support, promote, and act as a clearinghouse for the global laughter movement, with the mission of bringing events to every continent that supports health and peace through laughter. Articles, exercises, news and events.

Books by Karyn Buxman

What's So Funny About . . . Diabetes?

What's So Funny About . . . Heart Disease?

What's So Funny About . . . School Nursing?

Amazed & Amused

Laughing Your Way to More Money, Better Sex & Thinner Thighs

Humor Me (co-author)

The Service Prescription (co-author)

Chicken Soup for the Nurses Soul (contributor)

Coming soon in the "What's So Funny About...?" series

What's So Funny About . . . Alzheimer's?

What's So Funny About . . . Cancer?

What's So Funny About . . . Depression?

What's So Funny About . . . Parkinson's?

What's So Funny About . . . Aging?

What's So Funny About . . . Dialysis?

What's So Funny About . . . Love?

Index

E

F

G

H

I

J

R

S

T

U

V

W

Y

Karyn Buxman, RN, MSN, CSP, CPAE

The Really Important Stuff

Karyn Buxman is an RN with attitude . . . and a serious sense of humor. As a nurse, she cared for hundreds of patients one-on-one; as a motivational keynoter, she now administers to thousands of people from the stage. Karyn is a neurohumorist—one who researches the neurobiology of humor, and then translates these cutting-edge findings for the layperson, showing how they can harness applied humor to heal and empower themselves.

Karyn presents laughter with a purpose. Mirth with a message. Humor that heals. Keynotes that enlighten, educate and entertain. Karyn's key messages include "Humor is power," and "It is more important to *see* funny, than to *be* funny." Karyn follows in the footsteps of that *other* humorist from Hannibal, Missouri, Mark Twain.

The Additional Stuff

But wait—there's more! . . . There's that mind-body-spirit connection thing! As a researcher *and* performer, Karyn brings science, psychology and humor to health, success and spirituality.

What else? . . . Karyn has addressed 5,000 members of the Million Dollar Roundtable in Thailand; rocked 8,500 OR nurses in Chicago; and presented her research at the International Society for Humor Studies in Paris. (Oh! She's also addressed the US Air Force, Pfizer, the Mayo Clinic, and 1,197 other organizations.)

Karyn has authored six books, she is published in peer-reviewed journals, and she is an inductee into the Speaker Hall of Fame (one of only 37 women in the world). She is a contributor to two *Chicken Soup* books, and she is the author of the *What's So Funny About...?* series *(WSFA...Diabetes? WSFA...Heart Disease? WSFA...Nursing?)* She was given the Lifetime Achievement Award from the Association for Applied & Therapeutic Humor. Karyn's mission in life is to improve global health through laughter, and to heal the humor impaired.

800-848-6679

KARYNBUXMAN.COM

Made in the USA
Columbia, SC
23 March 2019